FOREVER BRILLIANT

FOREVER BRILLIANT

The Aurora Collection of Colored Diamonds

Alan Bronstein and Stephen C. Hofer

Ashland Press/Aurora Gems, New York

05   04   03   02   01   00   6   5   4   3   2

ISBN: 0-9659410-2-7

Library of Congress Card No.: 00-132823

"... Gems are the flowers of the mineral kingdom and the fancy coloured diamond is the orchid..."

R.J. Haüy   1817

An example of the twelve color varieties from the Aurora Collection, shown with a colorless diamond. Left to right: red (Aurora No. 62), green (Aurora No. 28), purple (Aurora No. 88), olive (Aurora No. 75), pink (Aurora No. 60), yellow (Aurora No. 105), orange (Aurora No. 240), colorless, white (Aurora No. 187), brown (Aurora No. 148), black (Aurora No. 173), blue (Aurora No. 7) and gray (Aurora No. 134).

"I am inspired by the varieties of colors, which reminded me so much of the phenomena of the aurora borealis, which suddenly light up the northern sky and are rarely seen by most people, and somehow I wanted to hold onto that feeling."

Harry Rodman 1986

To Harry Rodman

For all the jokes, courage, integrity, motivation, and positive energy
Harry has shared with so many people over the last 93 years and for his undying
faith in the Aurora Collection and the books that will be enjoyed
for generations to come.
A legacy of beauty and inspiration for all mankind.

Alan Bronstein

Collector and Diamond Consultant: Alan Bronstein

Collector: Harry Rodman

Gemologist, Author: Stephen C. Hofer

Museum Curator: George E. Harlow

Jewelry Historian: Janet Zapata

Technical Consultant: Nick Hale

Book Designer: Ludovica Weaver

Publishing Consultant: Frank Zachary

Editors: Ricardo Zapata, and Gillian Hillis

Photographers:
American Museum of Natural History, Display, p. x
Howard Ande, Sunrise, p. 10
Tim DeLaVega, Rainbow, p. xiv
Tino Hammid, Aurora Stones 1–260
Stephen C. Hofer, Orchid, p. v; Twelve Colors, p. vi; A Suite of Colors, p. xiii
Erica and Harold Van Pelt, Book Jacket and End Papers

Produced by Smallwood & Stewart, New York, New York

Printed by Centro Grafico Ricordi, SRL., Milan, Italy

Published by Ashland Press/Aurora Gems
589 Fifth Avenue, Suite 806
New York, New York 10017
Voice: (212) 355-1480
Fax: (212) 355-2239
Web site: www.diamonds-in-colors.com

Table of Contents

The Aurora Collection on display in the J.P. Morgan Memorial Hall of Gems at the American Museum of Natural History.

The Aurora Collection.

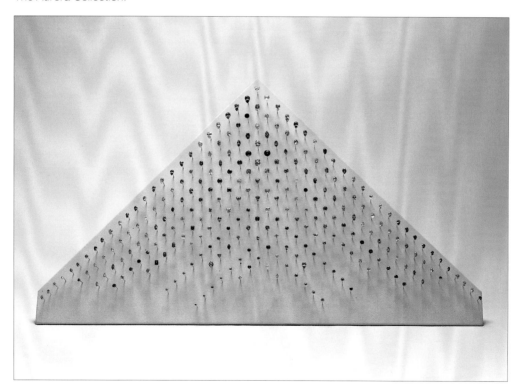

FOREWORD

My initiation as a museum curator began in the summer of 1976 with the opening of the Morgan Hall of Gems and Guggenheim Hall of Minerals at the American Museum of Natural History. At that time, the departing curator, Dr. Vincent Manson, had put together an ensemble of diamonds to make a big splash for the opening. Among the many festivities associated with this event, I remember vividly a party at the Sherry Netherlands Hotel, where we took our collection of 41 colored diamonds for a private viewing by a select group of Museum supporters and their friends. With Jacqueline Onassis and other celebrities in attendance, there was continuous fun and dancing, as well as an ever-present crowd gathered around the diamond display. Those events set into my mind a vision that would forever fuel my imagination for future museum activities. For, beyond the hoopla of the fun with diamonds as a heady start to my career, I realized that colored diamonds were among the most special of gems, something that captured people's attention and riveted their gaze to admire their rarity, brilliance, and infinite spectral variations. That first ensemble of colored diamonds was appropriately named "The Spectrum Collection" and remained at the Museum as a centerpiece in the Morgan Hall of Gems until 1986.

In the early 1980s, I ran across a passionate young man who was a virtual whirling dervish on the subject of colored diamonds. This encounter was the beginning of a long and fruitful professional relationship with Alan Bronstein, who, through years of inspired hard work bolstered by the insightful support of Harry Rodman, was able to create his own bevy of colorful beauties, which he called the Aurora Collection. When the Spectrum Collection vacated the Museum, Alan saw it as an appropriate place to share his collection with a large audience, and so he placed it on loan for public viewing in 1989. It remains there as the central attention-getting display in the Morgan Hall of Gems, regularly eliciting gasps from our visitors as well as a steady supply of "nose prints" on its case window.

As noted above, the allure of diamonds was not lost on me, and I set as one of my career goals to create a major exhibition that melded the stories from science, technology, geology, culture, history, jewelry, literature, mining, and gemology that surround diamonds. This exhibition came to fruition in 1997 as *The Nature of Diamonds*, and I believe it was a great success. Among the many fabulous images and objects from around the world to be exhibited, I knew I had to include those fancies in the Aurora Collection. To my delight, Alan and Harry were enthusiastic about this idea. During the first few weeks after opening, we had such a crush of viewers around the Aurora display that we had to relocate it to a more open spot to avoid unmanageable congestion. And, even against an impressive international set of great objects as competitors, the consensus was that the favorite case in the exhibition was that filled with colored diamonds. People were simply astonished at the wealth of different colors in a stone that, until then, most of them had only known in the white variety. Their reactions brought to mind the dramatic success of the visual media switch from black-and-white to color: it was irresistible!

George E. Harlow
Curator of Minerals and Gems
American Museum of Natural History

A suite of colored diamonds from the Aurora Collection, showing the diversity of colors produced by nature. Left to right: grayish green (Aurora No. 1), purple-pink (Aurora No. 9), brownish yellow (Aurora No. 3), pure blue (Aurora No. 7), pinkish purple (Aurora No. 2), and yellow-orange (Aurora No. 25).

"... like an elusive rainbow that suddenly appears after a storm, a collection of natural fancy color diamonds inspires viewers with an uplifting emotional response..."

Alan Bronstein   1988

A COLLECTOR'S PASSION

The Aurora Collection began as a quest for finding and bringing together specimens of the myriad of colors seen in diamonds, culminating in 1998 with the publication of the book *Collecting and Classifying Coloured Diamonds: An Illustrated Study of the Aurora Collection,* by Stephen C. Hofer. That book describes the collection of 260 colored diamonds in great detail, discussing it in the context of a variety of topics related to colored diamonds in general. The purpose of this new book is to make information about the beauty and value of this collection available to a broader audience of diamond enthusiasts who cannot spend the time poring over that comprehensive treatise.

I will always remember that day in 1980 when a golden yellow diamond that burned like the evening sun setting in the western sky was flashed in front of my eyes by a fellow trader. It had a hypnotic glow that kept me staring in wonder. I did not know at the time that this experience had been for me a true epiphany, that the revelation of such beauty would instill in me a passion to learn everything possible about these mystical stones. I did not know then that the seed for the Aurora Collection had been firmly planted in my soul.

Having been a diamond trader for two years, I thought it was unusual that fancy colored diamonds had not crossed my path previously. Then, as I visited with cutters and dealers in the industry, I was surprised time and again at how little information there was about them. Most dealers had seen very few colored diamonds, and the stories they told me seemed more like folklore than reality. I could find no study, articles, or even accurate photographs of colored diamonds. Most of the available literature centered on a dozen or so "historic" diamonds, tracing the provenance of those stones while saying almost nothing about their colors. Most of the publicity for the previous 75 years had focused on colorless diamonds while keeping colored diamonds as a "discreet" secret, with the exception of such famous diamonds as the blue Hope Diamond and the yellow Tiffany Diamond.

The renaissance of colored diamonds began in the early 1980s with successful promotions by the major auction houses, culminating in the "big bang" in

1987 when Christie's auctioned a 95/100-carat, purplish-red diamond for $880,000. This sale was the single most important event responsible for raising awareness about colored diamonds because it made every gem dealer in the world look at the potential value these gems offered. At about the same time, "supersaturated" pinks from a new Australian mine (Argyle) began to come on the market, being promoted internationally as their signature color. The last years of the twentieth century have seen numerous trade articles about and scientific studies of colored diamonds, together with a dramatic evolution of their market value and an increase in the public's awareness of them. It would be an understatement to say that colored diamonds are no longer perceived as the "poor cousins" of their prestigious colorless relatives.

The experience of seeing that first sun-drenched yellow diamond created in me the desire to focus on these diamonds, to learn more about them while also earning a living in the process. My first purchase was a golden yellow color stone that would serve as a sample to compare against other yellows. I was amazed to see how many different shades of yellow existed, modified by green, brown, orange, or gray tonalities. Most dealers tended to overlook these subtle differences, generalizing to the predominant yellow color and denoting every stone as "canary," the name officially reserved for the best yellow color. Sample stones taught me to be more selective as I learned to determine how the modifiers affected the face-up color. Thus, the Aurora Collection began as a selection of sample stones that opened up a world to which very few had paid attention.

When Harry Rodman became my partner in 1986, after fifty years as a successful gold refiner, the collection underwent a great expansion. We knew the stones could not be too large, for the sake of price, and we also wanted to maintain some uniformity in size; therefore, the average stone size is approximately 1 carat. Our principal guideline was to look for variety in colors, shapes, and saturations from weak to strong. We learned that the face-up color of diamonds having identical body colors will be perceived as different, depending on their respective shapes.

We patiently and deliberately selected the diamonds in the Aurora Collection according to a plan focused on the extensive diversity of diamond colors offered by nature, while attempting to have as many examples as possible of different color varieties and saturations. Size, shape, or freedom from inclusions were never deciding criteria for being included. A basic premise is that all colored diamonds are examples of nature at her geological best. Thus, each has a place in the family of colored diamonds and may be represented. Every diamond in the Aurora Collection has a history of how it came to our hands, but the fact that they live together as one unit is all that really matters.

Colors are part of our everyday world and affect our state of mind. This is especially true of colored diamonds, whose ever-shifting brilliance plays a key role in our perception of their color. In an attempt to characterize color and communicate with one another about it, we tend to draw analogies to objects of common experience and usage, usually from nature. Until the 1970s, people used such common color analogies to visualize and describe the color of diamonds. Then, color grading terminology formulated by the Gemological Institute of America (GIA) became the standard of communication. However, even though terms like 'grayish blue,' 'brownish orange,' and 'orangy pink' may be appropriate color grades, 'sky blue,' 'autumn orange,' and 'salmon pink' help us to visualize better the colors we see. After I met gemologist Stephen Hofer, together we decided that it was important to establish a nomenclature of common color names in order to help explain differences between stones with similar color grades. We felt this was crucial to the basic identification and understanding of colored diamonds, as well as to facilitate communication between dealers and collectors.

I first met Stephen Hofer in 1981, during a visit to the Gem Trade Laboratory in Santa Monica, California, where he was conducting research on colored diamonds. At that time, the laboratory was focusing on differentiating natural from treated stones and was not too concerned about color nomenclature. In 1984, Stephen began working in the New York Laboratory of GIA. In 1987, a mutual friend, Eunice Miles, a gemologist for forty years who loved colors in all domains of nature, asked us to participate in an experiment with her associate, Nick Hale, one of the world's leading color scientists, who was developing an instrument for measuring the color of diamonds. As a result, the instrumentally derived color measurements became the outline of the puzzle for classifying the entire colored diamond universe. Thinking back on that experience, I still marvel at the fortuitous nature of what Eunice accomplished. She brought together the technological innovation of Nick Hale regarding instrumental color measurement and the gemological applications developed by Stephen Hofer regarding methods for specifying face-up color, with the variety of colored diamonds that Harry Rodman and I had been able to assemble. Applying this new technology, Stephen was able to verify in color space the differences that we could see with our eyes but had trouble defining precisely. To complete this endeavor, the leading gem photographer, Tino Hammid, captured the essence of the stones on film as they are seen in this book.

As the collection evolved over the years, its true potential developed from a personal understanding to a scientific study with modern color science technology. Ultimately, we were able to share its beauty with the public at the American Museum of Natural History in New York City, beginning in 1989. Eight years later, it was prominently featured in the most ambitious diamond exhibition ever undertaken at that museum. Entitled *The Nature of Diamonds*, this exhibition featured the historic, scientific, and aesthetic aspects of diamonds. The Aurora Collection was exhibited in the vault area along with other important diamonds and jewelry. It was also chosen as a leading example to promote the exhibition. A photograph of the Collection served as a visual focal point to represent the exhibit in print, electronic media, advertising, newspapers, and magazines, as well as on various popular items the museum retailed including gift paper, scarves, notebooks, boxes, and even table mats. A fifty-foot banner featuring an assortment of colored diamonds hung proudly at the entrance to the museum, ushering in more than 380,000 visitors from around the world, making *The Nature of Diamonds* one of the most successful shows ever held at the museum. In 1999, the Aurora Collection was included in the exhibition at its venue, the San Diego Natural History Museum. From there, the Aurora Collection and *The Nature of Diamonds*, were exhibited in 2000 at the National Science Museum in Tokyo, Japan. In 2001 they were exhibited in the Musée de la Civilization in Quebec City, Quebec. In 2002 the exhibition has been at the Midland Center for the Arts in Midland, Michigan.

The Aurora Collection draws its name from the colorful northern lights, *aurora borealis*, a luminous phenomenon seen to best advantage in the arctic regions, and from Aurora, the Roman goddess of the dawn, who had the power to bestow eternal life on mortals. Thus, the name Aurora is relevant because these colorful diamonds have existed for a very long time and will continue to shine their beauty for all time to come.

For my partner, Harry Rodman, and I, this collection represents the diversity of nature and how these differences, when brought together, enhance and complement each other's unique traits. We also think of the Aurora Collection as "art" in a new medium — perhaps as a painting made of little drops of high-energy colored lights glowing from the canvas, arranged in the shape of a pyramid, symbolizing a vortex of energy. The astonishing array of colors in this pyramid-like form creates a hypnotic allure that can entrance the viewer with compelling and irresistible delight.

Natural colored diamonds occur in infinite combinations of hues, modifiers, and saturations, constituting a unique color puzzle that can never be completed. Creating the Aurora Collection involved the joy of searching the world for new specimens and the thrill of adding missing parts to that puzzle. There were a handful of stones that would have made wonderful additions to the collection, but their owners would not sell them. It was still a pleasure to have seen them and to know they exist.

A key component of Stephen's book is a complete catalogue of the collection containing color photographs and physical descriptors of each stone in the collection. In the last section of this new book Stephen presents that catalogue following a detailed set of introductory notes aimed at a nontechnical audience. As he puts it, "this colorful catalogue of diamonds is intended as a practical standard of collecting achievement for anyone attempting to duplicate or even exceed the richness of the Aurora diamonds." I believe that the catalogue will also become an essential aid for those who want simply to enjoy viewing colored diamonds to the fullest.

Colorless diamonds have been admired, desired, or even worshiped for many centuries. However, as stated above, the popularity of colored diamonds is a relatively recent phenomenon. Yet there is a rich lore of colored diamonds embedded into the overall history of precious stones. Understanding this historical perspective can give us a valuable context for appreciating the rarity and value of the Aurora Collection. Janet Zapata contributes this perspective in the next section of this book.

Alan Bronstein

A Brief History
of Colored Diamonds

The mystique of diamonds has fascinated mankind since these precious stones were first discovered, probably as early as 3000 B.C. Collected, treasured, and sought after even to the point of malice, they became symbols of power and wealth, their beauty and glamour desired more than any other gemstone. Much has been written about diamonds, designers of diamond jewelry, and prominent owners of such beautiful objects of desire. Most of this literature focuses on colorless diamonds (often referred to as white diamonds), by far the most abundant variety of this precious stone; in fact, when most people say 'diamond,' they mean colorless diamond. Far less known because they are rarer, colored diamonds have remained in the shadow of their colorless siblings until relatively recent times. Yet research on art-historical records reveals a rich lore of noted — sometimes notorious — colored diamonds. As befitting the aura of mystery often surrounding famous stones, some of these records are based on speculation and a few are downright contradictory. Nevertheless, we can draw a coherent and informative picture that enables us to bring the history of colored diamonds into a current perspective.

Over the centuries, mining has yielded mostly colorless diamonds within a wide range of size, shape, clarity, and other desirable attributes for their use in jewelry, for exhibition at museums and other sites, or simply for the pleasure of private collectors. For these stones, the following simple rule applies: the lesser hint of any trace of color, the more desirable and valuable the stone. At the same time, nature has endowed colored diamonds with the same qualities of hardness and refraction as their colorless cousins, yet colored diamonds are enhanced by a magnificent spectrum of color that immediately captivates the eye of the discerning collector and connoisseur. In fact, every colored diamond has its own individual hue, and this is what makes it so unique, so mesmerizing. The beauty and value of this color dimension has not been lost on discriminating collectors throughout history.

Diamonds were first discovered in India, perhaps as long as five thousand years ago, by some accounts. It is believed that the Koh-i-noor, one of the world's greatest diamonds, was worn nearly five hundred years ago by Babur, the first Mogul emperor of India. The best diamonds remained in India — the pure, colorless specimens set aside for the Brahmins who, thus, became the first collectors of these precious stones. Because of their hardness, colored diamonds were also recognized as valuable, even if not yet appreciated or understood by collectors.

At first, diamonds were regarded as talismans to protect the wearer against evil. They were also used as a medium of exchange. Their exceptional hardness and durability made them useful as tools to cut and engrave other gemstones. Cleaning and polishing the surfaces of diamonds themselves was accomplished by the crude method of rubbing one stone against another, after which they would be set as gem pieces without any alteration to the octahedral form in the original crystals.

In the twelfth century the development of optics based on Euclid's treatise eventually led to an understanding of how to facet diamonds to bring out their hidden beauty to the fullest. Records suggest that cutters in Europe had perfected the art of faceting diamonds as early as the fourteenth century. However, official credit for the first scientific cutting of diamonds is generally given to Louis de Berquen of Bruges who, in 1476, faceted the three biggest diamonds in the collection of Charles the Bold, duke of Burgundy. It was he who cut the famous yellow diamond that many believe to be the Florentine, weighing 137.27 carats. This stone eventually came into the hands of the Medici family in Florence, where the French traveler and diamond merchant, Jean-Baptiste Tavernier, saw it in 1657 in the possession of the grand duke of Tuscany.

The name Tavernier is closely linked with diamonds because he traveled to India in the mid-seventeenth century, providing the first descriptions of the diamond operation in that country. On each of his many journeys, he purchased diamonds outright or resorted to trading his European wares, emeralds, and pearls to get the best stones, eventually bringing back to France enough diamonds to win a barony from a grateful Louis XIV. His name is intimately associated with many important colored diamonds that have since become historic, including a 242-carat faint pink stone he named "The Great Table."

In 1665, Tavernier visited the last of the great Moguls, Aurangzeb. Among this ruler's collection of gemstones, Tavernier saw his most prized possession, a 280-carat diamond known as the Great Mogul. Tavernier called it "the great diamond." Much history and mystique followed the Great Mogul. It has been speculated that, because of the similarity in shape and color (faintly bluish-green), it must be the same stone known today as the Orlov, which Count Grigori Orlov presented to Catherine the Great of Russia in 1775. This stone, weighing 189.6 carats, resides in the collection of the Kremlin State Museum.

Arguably the most famous of all colored diamonds, the Hope has had an illustrious and somewhat controversial history, which also starts with Tavernier. A 45.5-carat diamond endowed with a unique dark blue hue, it is believed to have been initially cut from a 112-carat stone that Tavernier brought back from India for Louis XIV in 1668. It was recut in 1673 into a 69-carat triangular-shaped stone and remained as a part of the French crown jewels during the reigns of kings Louis XV and Louis XVI, so we can speculate that it was handled by Queen Marie Antoinette, among others. The Hope was stolen from the French crown jewels in 1792, only to resurface many years later in London as a 45.5-carat cushion-shaped stone. When it was put up for sale there around 1824, the banker Henry Philip Hope purchased it for his collection. This diamond remained in the Hope family for seventy-seven years and was subsequently acquired by Mrs. Evelyn Walsh McLean of Washington, D.C. The noted New York jeweler, Harry Winston, purchased the stone in 1949 and presented it to the Smithsonian Institution, Washington, D.C., in 1958. It is there on display, the undisputed center of attraction in the permanent gems exhibit of the National Museum of Natural History. It has become one of the most recognizable gemstones in the world, not only because of its reputed association with misfortune but also because it is the largest deep blue diamond in existence.

In 1742, too late for Tavernier to witness, Augustus II, Elector of Saxony, acquired the 41-carat pear-shaped Dresden Green. Originally mounted in an Order of the Golden Fleece, it was later reset into a hat ornament. The only large naturally colored green diamond in existence, it is presently on display in the Grünes Gewölbe at the Albertinum Museum in Dresden.

Coinciding with the decreasing supply of diamonds mined in India, a new source was discovered in Brazil in 1730 (local reports point to actual discovery sixty years earlier, when diamonds were found mixed in with gold washings). Since at that time Brazilian stones did not have a reputation to match those from India, it was necessary for many years to ship them to Goa, a Portuguese possession in India, from where they would be shipped to Europe endowed with their new 'provenance.' By the 1870s, this new source was eclipsed by discoveries in South Africa.

Diamonds were found in South Africa in the late 1860s. The first find recorded was a 21-carat yellow diamond crystal, found by the son of a Boer farmer. After changing hands many times, it was displayed at the 1867 Exposition Universelle in Paris where it captivated all who came to see it. It was subsequently cut to a 10.73-carat brilliant and appropriately named Eureka. DeBeers later presented this diamond to the Parliament of South Africa in Cape Town.

Other discoveries of small and large diamonds in the South African mines led to a sizable influx of prospectors eager to cash in on the bonanza. The mines yielded not only large quantities of colorless diamonds but also fancy colored diamonds. Perhaps the best known example, the Tiffany Diamond, weighed 287.42 carats in the rough when it was discovered in the Kimberley Mines in 1878. The largest and finest yellow diamond in existence at the time, it was transferred to Paris the following year and cut into a cushion shape of 128.54 carats with ninety facets to maximize its brilliance. It has remained in the Tiffany & Co. collection.

Tiffany & Co. gained experience purchasing important diamonds, as is evident from their acquisition, in 1874, of the 30-carat Brunswick Yellow Diamond, of Indian origin, that had been in the collection of the "jewel mad" Duke of Brunswick, the quintessential diamond collector of the nineteenth century. The Duke was passionate about diamonds, owning a 13.75-carat blue pear-shaped specimen reputed to have been cut from the famous Tavernier Blue Diamond (from which the Hope was cut). Since historical accounts of this stone are not entirely consistent and its current whereabouts are unknown, a mystery remains as to its exact origin. The Duke also owned the Agra, a 32.2-carat brilliant-pink diamond said to have been worn in the turban of Babur. His collection was sold at auction the year after his death in 1873.

Until recently, pink diamonds were found in small quantities, first in India many centuries ago and later in Brazil and South Africa. The majority of these stones were very pale and, thus, classified as "faint" or "light" in terms of saturation. The few with significant color were called "fancy light pink." For this reason, pinks were considered among the rarest of all diamond colors. The discovery of the Argyle pipe in the western region of Australia in 1979 changed this situation dramatically. A selection of Argyle pinks were so saturated that they earned the designation of "fancy." In April 1989, sixteen of these stones were offered at auction at a Christie's New York sale, realizing above-estimate prices. In fact, ten of these stones were purchased by collectors, signaling a new interest in colored diamonds.

Prior to 1900, there had been only a handful of individuals, such as the Duke of Brunswick, who systematically collected colored diamonds. The first collector of note in the twentieth century was Atanik Eknayan, a diamond cutter from Paris. When he exhibited his collection of diamonds of over 70 different hues at the Louisiana Purchase Exhibition held in St. Louis in 1904, it became the first public display of an assortment of colored diamonds.

In the last twenty years, several collectors assembled important collections of colored diamonds, which have been exhibited at the American Museum of Natural History in New York City. These include André Gumuchian's collection of 41 colored diamonds, on view from May 1976 through June 1986. Known as the Spectrum Collection, it comprised natural, intense, and rare color diamonds ranging in size from 0.20 to 6.86 carats, and weighing an aggregate of 63.89 carats. It remained a popular exhibit for the ten years it was on view and, according to Dr. George Harlow at the museum, "At the time, it was the best on public display."

In 1981, the Rainbow Collection was exhibited at the museum, with subsequent venues at the Museum of Natural History in Los Angeles, the Academy of Science in San Francisco, the Antique Dealers and Jewelers Biennial Fair in Paris, and Province House in Antwerp. This collection, put together by Eddie Elzas, a dealer from Antwerp, comprised 301 diamonds. Elzas' concept was to collect pairs of stones of similar color, size, and shape. Many diamond dealers believe that both the Spectrum and Rainbow Collections are no longer intact.

Today, there are a few other collections of note on public view. The Butterfly Collection offers a symmetrical arrangement of 212 colored diamonds of similar colors, sizes and shapes, forming the outline of a butterfly. It was exhibited at the Houston Museum of Science from July 1994 through January 1996 and traveled to Japan in 2000. The DeBeers Collection, assembled for display at diamond industry events, consists of an assortment of colored diamonds from South African mines. The Townsend Collection of eight small colored diamonds is on view at the Victoria & Albert Museum in London.

By far, the most impressive of the contemporary colored-diamond collections is the 260-stone Aurora Collection, assembled by Alan Bronstein, a New York diamond consultant, and his partner and mentor, Harry Rodman. Bronstein began collecting these precious stones because of their sheer beauty and because they seemed to "talk" to him, a phenomenon that seems to afflict all great collectors! What started as a love affair with colored diamonds evolved into a comprehensive assembly of stones spanning a broad spectrum of colors over wide ranges of saturations, sizes, and shapes. It is arranged within a triangular space inspired by the form of a pyramid, so as to guide the eye of the viewer progressively from the apex to the lower positions. It has been on view at the American Museum of Natural History since 1989, to great acclaim by the visiting public. As a major component of the museum's record-breaking 1997 exhibition, *The Nature of Diamonds*, it was chosen as the visual motif in the museum's publicity for that event. The display of this collection at the museum's Morgan Memorial Hall of Gems is also the longest-running exhibition of colored diamonds in the world.

The Aurora Collection represents a major contribution to the world of gems, rivaling in importance the major stones discussed above. It goes far beyond encompassing the broadest range of colored diamond hues ever assembled. As a vehicle for a scientifically based, systematic identification and calibration of such hues, it will be used as a reference by gem students and collectors for generations to come. Because of it, the doors to learning about and appreciating the beauty of colored diamonds have been opened much wider.

Janet Zapata

"... All the colors of flowers and foliage and even the blue sky and the glory of the sunset clouds, only last for a short time, and are subject to continual change, but the sheen and coloration of precious stones are the same to-day as they were thousands of years ago and will be for thousands of years to come. In a world of change, this permanence has a charm of its own that was early appreciated..."

G.F. Kunz   1913

10

THE AURORA COLLECTION

I saw the Aurora Collection for the first time in the fall of 1983. Even though at that time the collection was in its infancy, with no more than 30 or 40 sparkling curiosities gathered together, my reaction was love at first sight. It was obvious to me that this was going to be a very special diamond collection.

This unique diamond collection was conceived and assembled by Alan Bronstein, a New York diamond consultant who spent over 20 years training his eyes and color memory to recognize and remember as many different diamond colors as possible. In the early days of his collecting endeavor, Alan would tell me "it's like working on a giant puzzle, one that cannot be learned in any other way except through repeated exposure to new and different stones." Thus, this fascinating "diamond color puzzle" was assembled in the same way an artist would fuss and labor over creating a work of art. By holding every polished colored diamond in his hand and carefully looking at its colors under different types of light, Alan learned to appreciate its individual beauty and began to understand the subtle similarities and color differences. At the same time, he was using his eyes and memory to identify which colors were missing from this unique color puzzle.

The Aurora Collection is limited to diamonds, specifically colored diamonds. This set of extremely rare and highly unusual gemstones offers the public a unique glimpse into the celebrated and mysterious world of the diamond, nature's most fascinating transparent solid material. Presently, this magnificent collection has a total of 260 diamonds and includes examples from each of the twelve color varieties in which natural diamonds are known to occur — white, gray, black, purple, pink, red, orange, brown, yellow, olive, green, and blue, thus enhancing its scientific and commercial importance tremendously (see Fig. 1).

In 1987, I was offered the opportunity to examine the Aurora Collection with scientific instruments, including measuring their colors with a gemstone colorimeter. Having spent the previous ten years studying the relationship between measured body color and perceived face-up color in colored diamonds, I was excited about this unique opportunity. And, while I shared Alan's enthusiasm for their

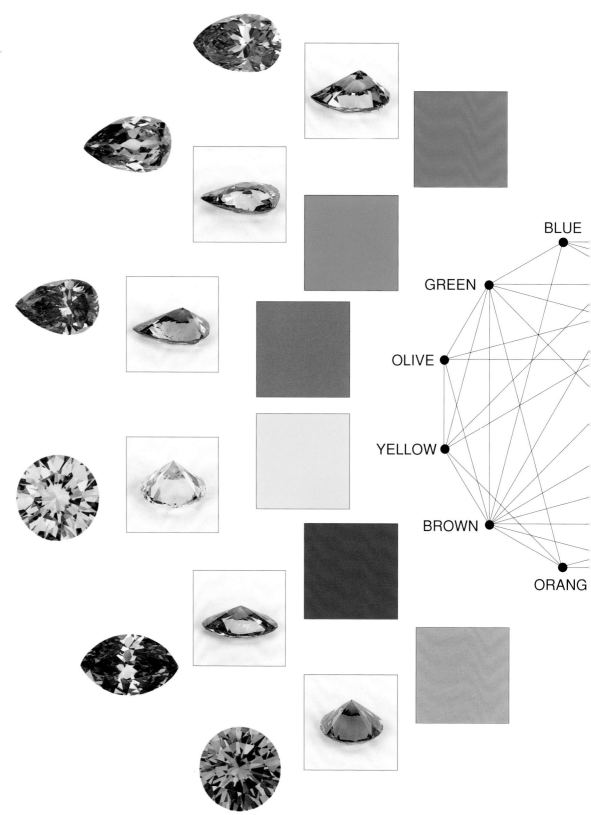

FIGURE 1.   Diamond color
variety chart.

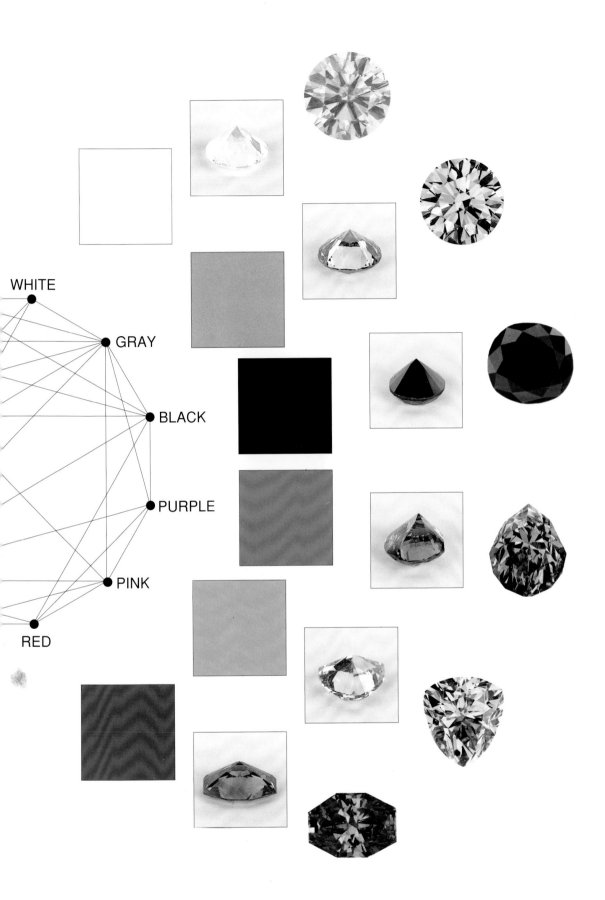

WHITE

GRAY

BLACK

PURPLE

PINK

RED

beauty, I was even more fascinated by the prospect of *measuring* their colors and then developing a system for *classifying* the Aurora diamonds according to those measured colors. I was also excited about working with top-notch collaborators: Eunice Miles, a noted gemologist who possessed a keen eye for color and an un-canny color memory; Nick Hale, a noted color scientist in the area of color appearance measurement, color tolerance specification, and color order systems, the former President and Technical Director of Munsell Color Corp. for 22 years; and Tino Hammid, an expert photographer of gems.

During this scientific study I concentrated on finding answers to a variety of questions, such as ... How many different colors are there in diamond? What causes the different colors to occur in diamond? What is the most saturated colored diamond that nature has ever produced? What is the most unusual color nature has produced in diamond? How saturated does a pink diamond have to be before it is classified as a true red diamond? How dark does a gray diamond have to be before it is classified as a true black diamond? How does the shape outline and style of cut in a polished colored diamond influence the path of reflected and refracted light, so that the final mosaic of colors seen in the face-up direction appears significantly different (i.e., lighter/darker and weaker/stronger) than the inherent body color? What is the rarest (i.e., most infrequent) color that natural color diamonds are known to occur in? ... Undoubtedly, there were many more questions than answers at that time.

Viewing this collection of colored diamonds is a thrilling experience for many; yet, for some observers, it can be an overwhelming task that requires the guidance of an orderly approach — a catalogue. Such a catalogue, included at the end of this discussion, presents all the diamonds in the Aurora Collection in a uni-form format consisting of a color photograph and a short table listing their physical characteristics. This colorful catalogue of diamonds is intended as a practical stan-dard of collecting achievement for anyone attempting to duplicate or even exceed the richness of the Aurora diamonds.

This book is meant to acquaint the reader visually with the Aurora diamonds without the need for deep technical knowledge. As you look at each of the 260 photographs, consider that each photo represents a particular face-up im-age of an Aurora diamond, captured (i.e., "frozen") on film for your viewing pleasure. Yet in reality, these colorful diamonds are not frozen colored mosaics; instead, they are alive! They sparkle and flicker when gently turned in the light, some appearing to have different colors (hues) when viewed in daylight vs. tungsten light, or having dif-ferent color tones with every slight change in the angle of viewing and illumination. Like an expensive sequined gown, a colored diamond is an undulating and restless mosaic of reflected colors that captures the eye, simulates the mind, and enlivens the spirit.

A polished colored diamond, when observed at a normal viewing distance (about 14 to 18 inches from stone to eye) exhibits a unique impression of colored reflections that appear deceptive and mysterious as the stone is turned in the light. This is why it takes years for a collector to develop his/her powers of visual observation in order to understand all the nuances of color that are present in diamond. Depending on the position of the stone relative to the light source and the observer, certain facets appear to change color, while others flicker, disappearing and reappearing as if controlled by some force within the diamond. This undulating and restless mosaic of colors in the face-up direction creates what many in the gem industry refer to as the "illusion" of a diamond's color.

In order to appreciate this aspect of a colored diamond, one must look closer at the realm of colors within our physical world and at the complex reaction we humans perceive when light falls upon a colored object. For example, the colors of natural objects, such as plants, animals, birds, insects, rocks, and shells have always fascinated man and have been a source of great pleasure. In the opinions of many mineralogists and gemologists, the range of colors exhibited by gemstones is miraculous, especially the range of colors exhibited by natural colored diamonds.

This diversity of color, inherent to all rough colored diamonds and apparent in the face-up direction of all polished colored diamonds, is caused by a limited number of factors. Specifically, the physical production of face-up color in a polished diamond involves the distance light rays travel inside the stone and the direction in which they exit the crown relative to the observer. In general, these light rays travel relatively long or short distances (i.e., more or less absorption of light) and then exit the crown in a direction along the observer's line of sight or in a direction away from the observer's line of sight. This basic behavior of light determines the colors we see in the face-up and how those colors are distributed.

In a colored diamond, what you actually see involves three major variables: the light source, the object, and the observer/detector. What you think you see involves personal judgment and subjective interpretation based on your own personal color preferences and experiences. To reduce or eliminate the effect of these variables in color measurement work, we standardize the light source, and the detector (the human visual system or an instrument designed to measure color in a similar manner), so that the object (gemstone) remains as the only variable. In this way, we can begin to arrive at an objective, meaningful specification of color appearance in diamonds, so as to enhance our knowledge and appreciation of the rich variety of specimens nature has to offer. A few illustrative examples follow from the Aurora Collection.

Of particular interest to the connoisseur, one specimen (Aurora No. 7) is very near in color to the famous Hope blue diamond, as determined when both were measured with a gemstone colorimeter. There is a matched pair of diamonds (Aurora Nos. 131 and 132), whose measured body color plots in the area where yellow, olive, and brown hues intersect in three-dimensional color space, making them unique collectors' items. Aurora No. 220 is an emerald-cut stone in which half the stone is colorless and the other half exhibits a delicate blue-gray color, resulting from minor amounts of boron trapped in the atomic structure. There is a bright green-yellow stone (Aurora No. 244) that contains a tiny garnet inclusion that looks as if a drop of red wine is trapped inside the diamond. A very rare type IIa orange diamond (Aurora No. 249) exhibits a color that many connoisseurs and collectors refer to as a "cantaloupe" colored diamond.

The collection also features certain colored diamonds whose measured and perceived color falls along the borderline between two adjacent colors in three-dimensional color space, providing an excellent opportunity for the expert and the novice to sharpen their skills of color observation and color discrimination. Examples include blue-gray (Aurora No. 246), orange-pink (Aurora No. 239), brown-yellow (Aurora No. 235), brown-orange (Aurora No. 227), pink-purple (Aurora No. 202), and green-yellow (Aurora No. 103). For those who prefer a simpler description of color, each of the Aurora diamonds is also given an appropriate common color name such as chocolate brown, canary yellow, bottle green, orchid purple, and rose pink, to name a few.

In addition to this physical aspect of color and the behavior of light, the color appearance of most natural objects is communicated in other ways. Specifically, a polished colored diamond exhibits other perceptual factors such as depth, transparency or translucence, gloss (luster), and various three-dimensional shape and facet arrangements. As a result, they do not appear as simple color images, nor do they lend themselves to simple color measurement techniques.

In the catalogue that follows, the Aurora diamonds are organized and numbered sequentially, starting with the smallest (Aurora No. 1 — 0.13 ct) and ending with the largest (Aurora No. 260 — 2.88 ct). Their physical descriptions consist of the following parameters:

Weight: the weight of each diamond to the nearest one-hundredth of a carat.

Measurements: the dimensions of each diamond to the nearest one-hundredth of a millimeter. For round stones, the three dimensions are minimum diameter, maximum diameter, and depth. For fancy-shaped stones, the three dimensions are length, width, and depth.

Shape: a description of the shape outline when viewed in the face-up direction (e.g., round, cushion, pear, marquise, oval, heart, triangle, square, rectangle, hexagon, octagon, or some combination or modification of these, such as rectangle-octagon).

Cutting: a description of the style of cutting (e.g., modern brilliant cut; antique brilliant cut, such as old mine or European brilliant cuts; step cut, such as the emerald cut; or various combinations or modifications of these three cutting styles, such as Radiant cut, Princess cut).

Common name: each diamond is assigned a common color name for describing the apparent face-up color of each stone (e.g., apple, canary, mauve). Certain diamonds can be described with more than one common name.

Color description: a color description for each Aurora diamond is derived from color measurements of the body color and visual assessment of the face-up color. These instrumentally and visually derived colors are listed according to the three attributes that comprise any given color: *hue* (HUE), *lightness* (LIT), and *saturation* (SAT). When all three attributes are mentioned together, e.g., purplish pink (hue)-medium (lightness)-moderate (saturation), they define the appearance of a colored diamond with greater accuracy than any one or two attributes. The following standard abbreviations for the twelve basic hues (HUE) are used throughout:

bk	=	blackish	BK	=	black
b	=	bluish	B	=	blue
br	=	brownish	BR	=	brown
gy	=	grayish	GY	=	gray
g	=	greenish	G	=	green
ol	=	olivish	OL	=	olive
o	=	orangish	O	=	orange
pk	=	pinkish	PK	=	pink
pp	=	purplish	PP	=	purple
r	=	reddish	R	=	red
wh	=	whitish	WH	=	white
y	=	yellowish	Y	=	yellow

Two additional abbreviations, CL = colorless, and v = violetish, not normally included in this set of twelve basic color varieties, are necessary to describe fully all colors in the Aurora collection. For color descriptions requiring multiple hues, the following conventions are used:

- the modifier (minor hue) is always listed first, followed by the variety (dominant hue),
- if a modifier is present in a small amount, it is written with the suffix (ish) and abbreviated in lower case,
- larger amounts of a modifying color are separated from the variety by a hyphen (-) and abbreviated in upper case,
- if no modifier is present, then only the variety is listed, abbreviated in upper case.

Examples of the above are:

pure brown	BR
yellowish brown	y-BR
yellow-brown	Y-BR
orangish yellowish brown	o-y-BR
orangish yellow-brown	o-Y-BR

The lightness (LIT) is abbreviated according to a nine-step scale:

VVLt	Very Very Light
VLt	Very Light
Lt	Light
Lt-Md	Light-Medium
Med	Medium
Md-Dk	Medium-Dark
Dk	Dark
VDk	Very Dark
VVDk	Very Very Dark

The saturation (SAT) is abbreviated according to an eight-step scale:

Wk	Weak
Wk-Md	Weak-Moderate
Mod	Moderate
Md-St	Moderate-Strong
St	Strong
St-VS	Strong-Very Strong
VSt	Very Strong
VVSt	Very Very Strong

The intent of this abbreviated method for denoting colors is to provide a consistent reference to help the untrained reader to differentiate and compare colored diamonds which, upon quick viewing, might appear to have the same physical characteristics. This also serves as a shorthand for use in the trade.

For each of the 260 Aurora diamonds, the table shows a color photograph depicting the face-up color of the diamond, enlarged to show detail. Diamond specimens were illuminated diffusely using 3200 Kelvin tungsten lamps, which lighted the inside surfaces of silver fabric "brollies," umbrella-like devices used by professional photographers. Four brollies were used, spread uniformly around the photo stage, separated by 90 degrees. Because of their size, they formed an almost complete hemisphere over the diamond specimens (Fig. 2). A Nikon F3 camera was used, situated directly over the specimen. For consistent results, all film used (Kodak EPY 64) came from the same emulsion lot and all was processed at the same time under identical chemical conditions. The surround (background) was a light gray coated paper, with a matte finish so as to reflect incident light diffusely.

The viewing (camera) axis was perpendicular to the table facet of each diamond along a line passing through the culet, and the lighting environment was diffused in a hemispherical manner so that light entered each specimen through the crown at multiple angles. This ensured an even distribution of light rays entering each diamond from the crown side, thereby not giving preference to any one dia-

SIDE VIEW

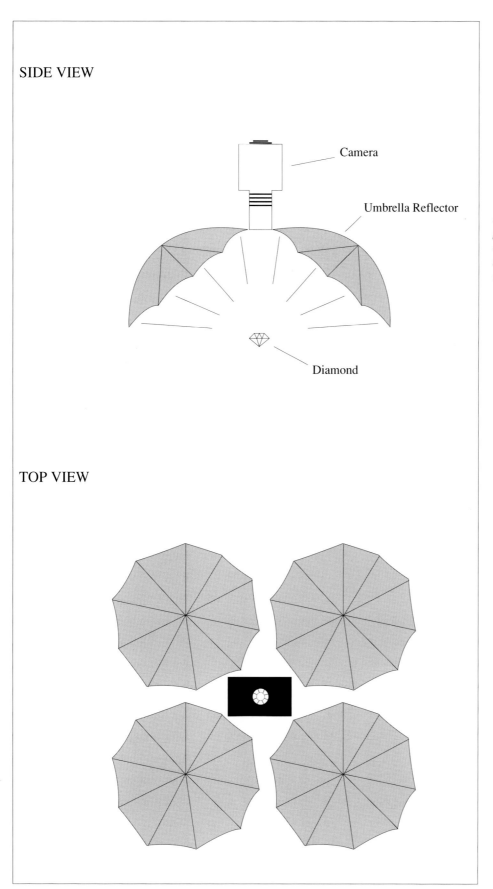

Camera

Umbrella Reflector

Diamond

FIGURE 2. Drawing of photographic lighting environment showing how light strikes a gem at multiple (hemispheric) angles.

TOP VIEW

mond regardless of its shape outline, style of cut, or body color. This lighting environment yielded results consistent with what a viewer would expect to see under similar conditions (i.e., moderate overcast sky; sunny day with sun being blocked by head or building; diffuse indoor fluorescent lighting). The diffuse lighting arrangement also minimized any of the whitish (mirrorlike) surface reflections that result from illumination from a direct (point) light source.

To the best of our visual and technical ability, the color photographs depict the true color of each Aurora diamond. However, due to physical limitations inherent to the photographic process, the often elusive colors of highly saturated fluorescent diamonds may not appear as strong in the photographs as they appear in the actual sample. This occurs because the color gamut of these diamonds exceeds the gamut of color on film, especially green and orange hues; therefore it is difficult to reproduce highly fluorescent colors photographically. In addition, the lamps used to create the hemispherical white light are largely devoid of ultraviolet wavelengths, hence the fluorescent glow (seen through the camera) is substantially reduced in strength or eliminated entirely.

A stringent quality control program for reproducing color was put in place before each photo was taken, and at each step in the reproduction process appropriate controls were implemented. These same standards for color quality control were also employed during the printing process. Finally, each of the surrounds was measured spectrophotometrically after the printing was completed, and these data were compared to like measurements made on the surrounds before photography to determine whether the color had shifted during printing. Once satisfied with the image color, we removed the gray background through a computer process, resulting in an accurate image of the face-up color on a white background. This is similar to the normal posture of looking at a colored diamond against a white grading tray (i.e., folded card). By measuring color, we know what we started with and we know what is finally offered to the reader. Thus, these are more than just beautiful pictures; they are accurate reproductions of the diamonds in the Aurora Collection.

To further aid the reader in appreciating and understanding the many colors in the collection, a photograph of the same colorless (E-grade) diamond is included in the middle of each page of the Aurora catalogue. This colorless diamond provides a visual point of reference, which should result in improved color comprehension and retention by the reader and enable each reader to compare the Aurora diamonds by flipping from page to page.

In addition to the photographs and the descriptive text, quotations selected from published diamond literature relevant to some aspect of each Aurora diamond are included. Statements contained in early sources are quoted verbatim in order to preserve their original impact; where necessary, I added explanations in brackets. In many cases, the quotation contains the common color name assigned to that diamond. In other instances, the quotation draws readers' attention to some unique aspect of the diamond's beauty, color, cutting, country of origin, history, or market position. It is hoped that these quotes will offer a substitute for additional technical information, while also drawing attention to the great body of knowledge and observations on color and colored diamonds contributed by previous writers.

Readers anxious for additional technical information regarding colored diamonds are referred to *Collecting and Classifying Coloured Diamonds: An Illustrated Study of the Aurora Collection* (New York: Ashland Press, 1998).

Stephen C. Hofer

"...Gems like these were not meant to be imprisoned in a dark vault for the momentary pleasure of a few eyes. The true value of a collection is in sharing it with as many people who are interested to experience nature's diversity of expression. It is a rare view of nature's masterpieces."

Alan Bronstein   1988

THE AURORA COLLECTION

"... the green diamond is also very rare, but I have seen some beautiful specimens in the Jardin des Plantes [Museum of Natural History] and in Freiberg, the first in the cabinet of Abbe Haüy, and the latter in the cabinet of Werner..."

L. Feuchtwanger 1872

"... the color of the Dresden Green diamond is most intriguing... we visually estimated the color of the diamond to be a medium slightly grayish Green..."

R. Kane 1990

Number	1
Weight	0.13 ct
Measurements	3.20 - 3.25 x 2.00 mm
Shape	round
Cutting	modern brilliant
Common Name	**jade**
Hue (HUE)	grayish green (gy-G)
Lightness (LIT)	light-medium (Lt-Md)
Saturation (SAT)	weak (Wk)

"... the colour of the diamond is generally referred to as white or colourless... the common shades among diamond are pale yellow and pale brown. It is difficult to describe the range of colour in the diamond, as one shade grades into the other, pale yellow to deep yellow, pale brown to deep brown... but other shades are occasionally found, such as orange, pink, mauve, green, blue, red and black..."

A.F. Williams 1932

"... on the color scale these 'fancy' diamonds begin where the slight glint of pale yellow, pink, green, mauve, or blue gives way to a substantial, pronounced coloration."

E.J. Gübelin 1980

Number	2
Weight	0.16 ct
Measurements	3.48 - 3.53 x 2.06 mm
Shape	round
Cutting	modern brilliant
Common Name	**mauve**
Hue (HUE)	pinkish purple (pk-PP)
Lightness (LIT)	light (Lt)
Saturation (SAT)	weak (Wk)

"... Yellow brilliants, if fine, are generally extremely lively, and suit the purposes of the jeweller in composing fancy articles..."

J. Mawe 1823

"... don't be afraid to consider [collecting] smaller stones... very often, small stones exhibit some of the finest colors... and since fine color is your primary goal when buying a fancy color diamond, it is often good sense to think small — and that can mean half caraters..."

H. Frydman 1983

Number	3
Weight	0.24 ct
Measurements	3.92 - 3.97 x 2.51 mm
Shape	round
Cutting	modern brilliant
Common Name	**banana**
Hue (HUE)	brownish yellow (br-Y)
Lightness (LIT)	light-medium (Lt-Md)
Saturation (SAT)	strong-very strong (St-VSt)

"... Rothschild, 6 Avril [April] 1853, 1 Brilliant [Diamond], 3 [carats], Pendeloque [pear-shaped], Eau de Mer [sea water colour], Monte en Bague [mounted in ring]."

Duke of Brunswick 1874

"... diamonds of various colours... jet black, golden brown, milky white, light yellow, light brown, light steel blue, sea green, yellow brown, and rose pink..."

A.F. Williams 1932

Number	4
Weight	0.25 ct
Measurements	5.51 x 3.85 x 2.01 mm
Shape	pear
Cutting	modern brilliant
Common Name	**sea**
Hue (HUE)	bluish green (b-G)
Lightness (LIT)	light-medium (Lt-Md)
Saturation (SAT)	weak (Wk)

Number 5	
Weight .... 0.25 ct	
Measurements .... 3.99 - 4.03 x 2.51 mm	
Shape .... round	
Cutting .... modern brilliant	
Common Name .... **lime**	
Hue (HUE) .... yellow-green (Y-G)	
Lightness (LIT) .... light (Lt)	
Saturation (SAT) .... moderate-strong (Md-St)	

"... Next to the yellow, for colored varieties, the green, including all shades, are most numerous, yet the pure emerald or grass-green diamond is rare."

S.M. Burnham   1886

"... A pure green colour is not common in diamond... Natural green diamonds, if of fine colour, tend towards an apple green shade..."

R. Webster   1948

Number 6
Weight .... 0.26 ct
Measurements .... 5.19 x 4.01 x 1.90 mm
Shape .... oval
Cutting .... modern brilliant
Common Name .... **rose**
Hue (HUE) .... purplish pink (pp-PK)
Lightness (LIT) .... light-medium (Lt-Md)
Saturation (SAT) .... weak-moderate (Wk-Md)

"... of fancies the Voorspoed mine yields fine rose-pink diamonds, which retain their colour after cutting."

P.A. Wagner   1914

"... A medium tone of rose-pink hue is the most desired body color for fancy pink diamonds..."

J.A. Henry   1979

Number 7
Weight .... 0.27 ct
Measurements .... 3.99 - 4.04 x 2.68 mm
Shape .... round
Cutting .... modern brilliant
Common Name .... **blueberry**
Hue (HUE) .... blue (B)
Lightness (LIT) .... medium-dark (Md-Dk)
Saturation (SAT) .... weak-moderate (Wk-Md)

"... Blue diamonds... those of a dark blue shade constituting beautiful gems, which differ from the blue sapphire in the quality of the tint, and in the play of colors peculiar to the diamond."

S.M. Burnham   1886

"... the Premier mine occasionally produces a diamond of exceptional colour which is inky blue in the rough and which is the nearest approach to the colour of the Hope diamond..."

A. Williams   1932

Number 8
Weight .... 0.33 ct
Measurements .... 5.36 x 3.82 x 2.40 mm
Shape .... cushion-oval
Cutting .... modern brilliant
Common Name .... **cream**
Hue (HUE) .... orangish yellow (o-Y)
Lightness (LIT) .... light-medium (Lt-Md)
Saturation (SAT) .... moderate (Mod)

"... A coloured diamond, in the hands of the cutter, has not yet become an object of beauty... the work of the cutter is not confined to the removal of the outer crust of the stones — he gives them the definite form which they are to preserve..."

L. Dieulafait   1874

"... Colored diamonds. The Hindus divide Diamonds into four classes, according to their castes... the cream-colored, to the Vaisys."

S.M. Tagore   1879

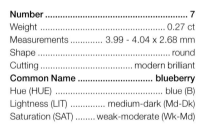

"... in the early 1980s when Australia started to produce deep pinks... suddenly, the diamond world was seeing fancy diamonds with hues that inspired comparison to raspberries, even red grapes... In no time at all, pink diamonds became a jewelry, as well as a collector's item..."

D. Federman 1989

Number 9
Weight .... 0.34 ct
Measurements .... 5.90 x 3.79 x 2.51 mm
Shape .... pear
Cutting .... modern brilliant
Common Name .... raspberry
Hue (HUE) .... purple-pink (PP-PK)
Lightness (LIT) .... medium (Med)
Saturation (SAT) .... weak-moderate (Wk-Md)

"... Diamonds... of a positive grass-green color are uncommon..."

A.C. Hamlin 1884

"... The range of color of the diamond is extensive, including nearly all the prismatic [spectral] hues. The yellows and browns perhaps afford the greatest number of shades and are the most numerous. Next to these, for colored specimens, the greens, including all shades, are most plentiful; the pure grass-green and emerald-colored diamonds are, however, very rare, as, indeed, are all the strongly colored specimens..."

G. Merrill 1922

Number 10
Weight .... 0.35 ct
Measurements .... 4.38 - 4.59 x 2.76 mm
Shape .... round
Cutting .... modern brilliant
Common Name .... grass
Hue (HUE) .... yellow-green (Y-G)
Lightness (LIT) .... light-medium (Lt-Md)
Saturation (SAT) .... moderate (Mod)

"... A curious diamond... by artificial light it appears brown; but the entire stone throws out bright red reflections such as are produced by the diamond only."

G.F. Kunz 1884

"... particular diamonds are from South Africa... whites... canary-yellow... golden... brown... reddish-brown... and steel-blue grey..."

G.F.H. Smith 1949

Number 11
Weight .... 0.35 ct
Measurements .... 4.63 - 4.70 x 2.66 mm
Shape .... round
Cutting .... modern brilliant
Common Name .... chestnut
Hue (HUE) ....
.... reddish orangish brown (r-o-BR)
Lightness (LIT) .... very dark (VDk)
Saturation (SAT) .... weak (Wk)

"... Yellow diamonds are looked upon with disfavor by many and rightly so when we consider the muddy [brown] and undecided [pale] shades that are termed yellow. But a moment's glance at the series of yellow crystals in this collection cannot fail to lead every one to a more just appreciation of their beauty, and even to give them the preference over the other colors."

G.F. Kunz 1885

"... capes run to yellow, but the tendency of the Brazilian is towards green..."

W.R. Cattelle 1903

Number 12
Weight .... 0.35 ct
Measurements .... 4.46 - 4.50 x 2.87 mm
Shape .... round
Cutting .... modern brilliant
Common Name .... chartreuse
Hue (HUE) .... greenish yellow (g-Y)
Lightness (LIT) .... light (Lt)
Saturation (SAT) ..... strong-very strong (St-VSt)

Number 13
Weight .... 0.36 ct
Measurements .... 5.57 x 3.69 x 2.59 mm
Shape .... oval
Cutting .... modern brilliant
Common Name .... strawberry
Hue (HUE) .... reddish pink (r-PK)
Lightness (LIT) .... medium (Med)
Saturation (SAT) .... weak-moderate (Wk-Md)

"... Rose colored diamond are not so plentiful as has been supposed; while the red, of rich deep tints surpassing the ruby in beauty, are extremely rare, and constitute one of the most magnificent ornamental stones known to exist."
S.M. Burnham   1886

Every once in a while a very special diamond is brought to light from its hiding place deep within the earth... This discovery generates great excitement within the world of the diamond connoisseur..."
Argyle Diamonds Ltd.   1991

Number 14
Weight .... 0.37 ct
Measurements .... 6.30 x 4.15 x 2.41 mm
Shape .... marquise
Cutting .... modern brilliant
Common Name .... sea foam
Hue (HUE) .... bluish green (b-G)
Lightness (LIT) .... light (Lt)
Saturation (SAT) .... weak (Wk)

"... the diamond diggings on the island of Borneo [Kalimantan] in the neighborhood of Martapoera... the Diamonds are either colorless or of various tints — yellow, green and even black; the most highly prized being those [green] which present a faint shade of blue, known to the Malays as ajer-laut, or 'sea water'..."
E.W. Streeter   1884

"... In appearance the stone is like a large rose, Indian cut, and pure white [colourless] with a tendency to a slightly bluish-green water."
L. Twining   1960

Number 15
Weight .... 0.37 ct
Measurements .... 5.77 x 4.17 x 2.56 mm
Shape .... pear
Cutting .... modern brilliant
Common Name .... moss
Hue (HUE) .... olive (OL)
Lightness (LIT) .... medium-dark (Md-Dk)
Saturation (SAT) .... weak-moderate (Wk-Md)

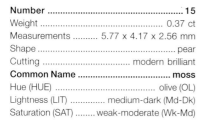

"... fancy colored diamonds combine the best of all worlds — the vibrant beauty of an intense colored stone with the life and sparkle only diamonds can offer. Intense fancy colored diamonds aren't something you will forget easily..."
H. Huffer   1983

Number 16
Weight .... 0.38 ct
Measurements .... 4.65 - 4.72 x 2.74 mm
Shape .... round
Cutting .... modern brilliant
Common Name .... chartreuse
Hue (HUE) .... greenish yellow (g-Y)
Lightness (LIT) .... very light (VLt)
Saturation (SAT) .... strong (St)

"... the [Brazilian] Diamonds from Diamantina and Grão Mogol differ from those of the Bahia mines in shape and color... the form of the stones is more regular, while the color is more uniform in its greenish tints, and less, if at all, viviated by any yellow reflection..."
E.W. Streeter   1884

"... Radiating an intangible beauty and dazzling color, these unique gems are perfect symbols of the inexhaustible magnificence of nature..."
E.J. Gübelin   1980

"... Brazil produces stones of many colors. I have seen stones of all colors, beautiful pink, fine blue, and several of a green tinge, the yellow were the most common..."

H. Pearson   1909

"... A valuable stone is the one thing that endures. Lace is soon a rag, velvet impossible, flowers dead; but a jewel, if treated kindly, lives forever. It is indeed almost as indestructible as truth or a mightly love..."

H. Bridgman   1916

Number	17
Weight	0.38 ct
Measurements	5.49 x 4.13 x 2.46 mm
Shape	oval
Cutting	modern brilliant
Common Name	**grapefruit**
Hue (HUE)	greenish yellow (g-Y)
Lightness (LIT)	light (Lt)
Saturation (SAT)	strong-very strong (St-VSt)

"A coloured diamond which is lacking in transparency is of very much less value than one of the same colour which is clear and transparent."

M. Bauer   1896

"... solitaires of... delicate pink water [body colour]. All the shades of colour mingle with a general sparkling gamut, enchanting in appearance and deeply artistic in its general effect."

L. Twining   1960

Number	18
Weight	0.39 ct
Measurements	5.11 x 4.35 x 2.35 mm
Shape	cushion
Cutting	modern brilliant
Common Name	**old rose**
Hue (HUE)	brownish pink (br-PK)
Lightness (LIT)	light-medium (Lt-Md)
Saturation (SAT)	weak-moderate (Wk-Md)

"... Diamond... This gem sometimes occurs of various colors. In my cabinet [collection] I have six different colors."

I. Lea   1876

"... some, not all, diamonds fluoresce in ultra-violet rays, appearing blue or yellow-green..."

G.F.H. Smith   1949

Number	19
Weight	0.39 ct
Measurements	6.08 x 4.22 x 2.64 mm
Shape	pear
Cutting	modern brilliant
Common Name	**chartreuse**
Hue (HUE)	green-yellow (G-Y)
Lightness (LIT)	light (Lt)
Saturation (SAT)	strong (St)

"... the Wesselton mine... produces fine golden-coloured fancy stones."

P.A. Wagner   1914

"... in the rough, it was not considered to be promising. It turned out to be a fine stone of golden colour, which I eventually sold and which became part of a famous collection..."

A. Monnickendam   1955

Number	20
Weight	0.39 ct
Measurements	5.67 x 3.91 x 3.00 mm
Shape	pear
Cutting	modern brilliant
Common Name	**golden**
Hue (HUE)	greenish orangish yellow (g-o-Y)
Lightness (LIT)	light-medium (Lt-Md)
Saturation (SAT)	strong-very strong (St-VSt)

Number 21	
Weight .... 0.40 ct	
Measurements .... 4.72 - 4.76 x 2.92 mm	
Shape .... round	
Cutting .... modern brilliant	
Common Name .... amber	
Hue (HUE) ...... orange-brown-yellow (O-BR-Y)	
Lightness (LIT) .... medium (Med)	
Saturation (SAT) .... moderate (Mod)	

"... Nature is sporting enough to provide encouraging numbers of fancy color diamonds with golden amber and fiery autumn hues, but the orange in these stones usually amounts to a secondary tinge or color highlight..."

D. Federman   1991

Number 22	
Weight .... 0.40 ct	
Measurements .... 5.82 x 4.06 x 2.58 mm	
Shape .... oval	
Cutting .... modern brilliant	
Common Name .... siskin	
Hue (HUE) .... olivish yellow-green (ol-Y-G)	
Lightness (LIT) .... light-medium (Lt-Md)	
Saturation (SAT) .... moderate (Mod)	

"... Oil-green or yellowish green is seen most frequently, then pale green, leek-green, asparagus green, pistachio-green, olive-green, siskin-green, emerald-green, bluish-green and grayish-green."

M. Bauer   1896

"... The 'fancies' are really colored diamonds, and include all the well-marked colors of desirable shades, red and apple green... and rather pale sapphire blue, absinthe green..."

F.B. Wade   1923

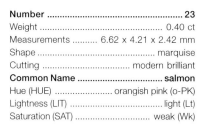

Number 23	
Weight .... 0.40 ct	
Measurements .... 6.62 x 4.21 x 2.42 mm	
Shape .... marquise	
Cutting .... modern brilliant	
Common Name .... salmon	
Hue (HUE) .... orangish pink (o-PK)	
Lightness (LIT) .... light (Lt)	
Saturation (SAT) .... weak (Wk)	

"... The diamonds called pink include those various shades of color such as pink, rose, peach, salmon... some of these colors may have a secondary tone or slight tint of brown..."

J.A. Henry   1979

Number 24	
Weight .... 0.41 ct	
Measurements ,......... 5.83 x 3.95 x 2.51 mm	
Shape .... oval	
Cutting .... modern brilliant	
Common Name .... jonquil	
Hue (HUE) .... orangish yellow (o-Y)	
Lightness (LIT) .... light-medium (Lt-Md)	
Saturation (SAT) .... strong (St)	

"... Yellow diamonds fit into many categories... yellows can be pure yellow, 'lemon' yellow, brownish yellow 'champagne' and orange yellow 'jonquil,' and the essential method of differentiating them is by comparison with other diamonds, so that the eye adapts to the different nuances..."

T. Loevy   1981

"... orange color diamonds... bring a good price and are growing in favor..."

W.R. Cattelle   1903

"... Russia's Treasure boasts several tens of thousands of carats of diamonds, ranging from small roses [cuts] to majestic solitaires weighing up to 200 metric carats. And a diversity in colors and hues: white, bluish, greenish, rosy, exquisitely pale orange, sky-blue, etc..."

A.E. Fersman   1925

Number 25
Weight .... 0.41 ct
Measurements .... 6.80 x 3.93 x 2.67 mm
Shape .... marquise
Cutting .... modern brilliant
Common Name .... **marigold**
Hue (HUE) .... yellow-orange (Y-O)
Lightness (LIT) .... medium (Med)
Saturation (SAT) .... strong (St)

"... [pale] Pink diamonds... they are a gem cutter's nightmare, for with a miscalculation... the color disappears... Let's say the cutter is lucky and completes the process — the soft color can still be lost when the gem is mounted in its setting..."

P. Proddow   1994

Number 26
Weight .... 0.42 ct
Measurements .... 4.47 x 4.60 x 3.02 mm
Shape .... heart
Cutting .... modern brilliant
Common Name .... **baby**
Hue (HUE) .... purplish pink (pp-PK)
Lightness (LIT) .... light-medium (Lt-Md)
Saturation (SAT) .... weak (Wk)

"... the brown diamonds are particularly appropriate as an accompaniment to hyacinths [hessonite], zircons, topazes, any stone containing brown, red or yellow..."

H. Bridgman   1916

Number 27
Weight .... 0.42 ct
Measurements .... 6.53 x 3.91 x 2.91 mm
Shape .... pear
Cutting .... modern brilliant
Common Name .... **scotch**
Hue (HUE) ....
.... yellowish orangish brown (y-o-BR)
Lightness (LIT) .... medium-dark (Md-Dk)
Saturation (SAT) .... strong (St)

"... the diamond is found at times in almost every color, red, sapphire blue, emerald green are very rare and are highly valued..."

W.R. Cattelle   1903

"... Quite recently there was found in the Bloemhof district of the Orange Free State [South Africa] a blackish looking diamond of five and a half carats' weight. When cut, the interior of the stone had a most beautiful emerald hue."

G.F. Kunz   1922

Number 28
Weight .... 0.42 ct
Measurements .... 4.58 x 4.13 x 3.06 mm
Shape .... cushion-round
Cutting .... antique brilliant
Common Name .... **emerald**
Hue (HUE) .... green (G)
Lightness (LIT) .... medium (Med)
Saturation (SAT) .... weak-moderate (Wk-Md)

Number 29
Weight .... 0.43 ct
Measurements .... 4.56 - 3.72 x 2.69 mm
Shape .... rectangle
Cutting .... modified emerald
Common Name .... **aquamarine**
Hue (HUE) .... green-blue (G-B)
Lightness (LIT) .... light-medium (Lt-Md)
Saturation (SAT) .... weak-moderate (Wk-Md)

"... The rarest diamond hues are red, pink and blue... other oddball fancy shades such as aqua-green or amethyst purple are so rare that prices are impossible to quote..."

D. Federman   1982

"... You can sell a fine, natural, fancy colored diamond ten times over, but once sold, where will you find another? That is the story of colored diamonds..."

L. Graff   1986
(see Kaye 1986)

Number 30
Weight .... 0.43 ct
Measurements .... 5.32 x 4.36 x 2.72 mm
Shape .... cushion-oval
Cutting .... modern brilliant
Common Name .... **bubble gum**
Hue (HUE) .... purplish pink (pp-PK)
Lightness (LIT) .... light-medium (Lt-Md)
Saturation (SAT) .... weak-moderate (Wk-Md)

"... the most one could hope for color-wise from a pink diamond was a shade reminiscent of cotton candy or bubble-gum... they were of interest mainly to collectors..."

D. Federman   1989

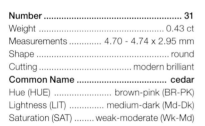

Number 31
Weight .... 0.43 ct
Measurements .... 4.70 - 4.74 x 2.95 mm
Shape .... round
Cutting .... modern brilliant
Common Name .... **cedar**
Hue (HUE) .... brown-pink (BR-PK)
Lightness (LIT) .... medium-dark (Md-Dk)
Saturation (SAT) .... weak-moderate (Wk-Md)

"... a common complication in appraising the pale shades of pink is in determining if the hue is truly pink, or pink with a secondary brownish tone, or pinkish-brown. A pink diamond of great clarity, brilliance, and good proportions will command an excellent price in the market; but if the pink tone is actually imposed upon by or mingled with a light brown body color, the price will be off... since the brown color gives a possibly muddy or cloudy effect..."

J.A. Henry   1979

Number 32
Weight .... 0.44 ct
Measurements .... 6.43 x 4.02 x 2.79 mm
Shape .... pear
Cutting .... modern brilliant
Common Name .... **cognac**
Hue (HUE) ....
greenish yellowish orangish brown (g-y-o-BR)
Lightness (LIT) .... medium-dark (Md-Dk)
Saturation (SAT) .... strong (St)

"... Under artificial light... Some fancy mixed colour stones become strangely transformed. There are specimens, green to gold in daylight, which change to brown and red by artificial light..."

W.R. Cattelle   1911

"... The diamonds of the brown series often have secondary tone ranging through coffee, cognac, cinnamon, bronze, sherry, and even extending into orange or reddish-brown. Most of them are characterized by some degree of green fluorescence..."

E.J. Gübelin   1980

"... some diamonds are fluorescent... appearing... to emit bright blue, apricot, pale blue, red, yellowish green, orange, and pale green light..."

W. Crookes   1909

"... Aside from those diamonds which have a pronounced and beautiful color (so called fancy stones), the tints of color in diamonds are pale and pass by almost insensible gradations, from yellow or brown that is obvious."

F.B. Wade   1923

Number 33
Weight .... 0.44 ct
Measurements .... 4.76 - 4.85 x 2.98 mm
Shape .... round
Cutting .... modern brilliant
Common Name .... chamois
Hue (HUE) ....
.... brownish orange-yellow (br-O-Y)
Lightness (LIT) .... light-medium (Lt-Md)
Saturation (SAT) ...... moderate-strong (Md-St)

"... Pink diamonds do not usually crystallize perfectly, nor are they transparent..."

G.F. Kunz   1885

"... Australian pinks may encourage false expectations on the part of dealers and jewelers who are not versed in fancy-color diamonds. Attention paid to Australian stones may result in a preference for dark pink... such a preference totally ignores the fact that this color is never found in larger stones [above five carats]..."

A. Bronstein   1988

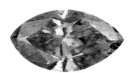

Number 34
Weight .... 0.45 ct
Measurements .... 6.74 x 3.57 x 2.68 mm
Shape .... marquise
Cutting .... modern brilliant
Common Name .... clover
Hue (HUE) .... purple-pink (PP-PK)
Lightness (LIT) .... light-medium (Lt-Md)
Saturation (SAT) .... weak-moderate (Wk-Md)

"... There are diamonds of almost all colours: some incline to rose colour, others to green, blue, brown, and black."

W.H. Pepys   1803

"... Pink diamonds from Australia... the majority of which have a very obvious pink color face-up, have numerous minute pink grain lines that are more closely spaced than has been observed in most diamonds with pink graining examined previously..."

S.C. Hofer   1985

Number 35
Weight .... 0.45 ct
Measurements .... 4.54 - 4.61 x 3.29 mm
Shape .... round
Cutting .... modern brilliant
Common Name .... rose
Hue (HUE) .... purplish pink (pp-PK)
Lightness (LIT) .... medium (Med)
Saturation (SAT) .... weak-moderate (Wk-Md)

"... brown family stones often show traces of three or four colors and resemble everything from honey and amber to ale and topaz..."

H. Frydman   1983

Number 36
Weight .... 0.45 ct
Measurements .... 6.53 x 4.41 x 2.37 mm
Shape .... pear
Cutting .... modern brilliant
Common Name .... honey
Hue (HUE) ....
.... yellowish orangish brown (y-o-BR)
Lightness (LIT) .... medium (Med)
Saturation (SAT) .... strong (St)

Number 37
Weight .... 0.45 ct
Measurements .... 6.32 x 4.57 x 2.46 mm
Shape .... pear
Cutting .... modern brilliant
Common Name .... clove
Hue (HUE) .... olive-brown (OL-BR)
Lightness (LIT) .... dark (Dk)
Saturation (SAT) .... weak-moderate (Wk-Md)

"... Brown diamonds are most often noted as coming from South Africa... there is often a secondary tone in brown diamonds which produces a variety of colors such as coffee, beige, clove, cinnamon, champagne, golden, bronze, and reddish-brown..."

J.O. Gill   1979

Number 38
Weight .... 0.46 ct
Measurements .... 5.06 - 5.10 x 2.93 mm
Shape .... round
Cutting .... modern brilliant
Common Name .... periwinkle
Hue (HUE) .... purple (PP)
Lightness (LIT) .... light (Lt)
Saturation (SAT) .... weak (Wk)

"... if the culet be cut in a small section of extraordinary fine color, though the stone be otherwise well-nigh colorless, the color of the culet would appear solid of that tint throughout the cut stone when faced up..."

W.R. Cattelle   1903

Number 39
Weight .... 0.46 ct
Measurements .... 6.74 x 3.91 x 2.71 mm
Shape .... marquise
Cutting .... modern brilliant
Common Name .... bronze
Hue (HUE) ..... olivish yellowish brown (ol-y-BR)
Lightness (LIT) .... medium-dark (Md-Dk)
Saturation (SAT) .... moderate (Mod)

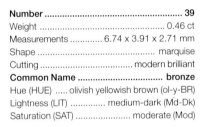

"... Brown Diamond... The characteristic tint is nearly a cinnamon brown. The range of colour is from white [colourless] with just a tinge of brown to a rich dark brown with a suspicion of red. Tints included [with brown] are milk white, bluish white, pinkish, pale mauve, amethyst, violet, pink, rose and bronze green. These tints are often pleasing, and some... command high prices in the market..."

J.R. Sutton   1928

Number 40
Weight .... 0.46 ct
Measurements .... 6.44 x 4.44 x 2.68 mm
Shape .... marquise
Cutting .... modern brilliant
Common Name .... aquamarine
Hue (HUE) .... green-blue (G-B)
Lightness (LIT) .... light-medium (Lt-Md)
Saturation (SAT) .... weak (Wk)

"... Diamonds of a light aqua-marine of greenish and bluish tints..."
A.C. Hamlin   1884

"... a necklace containing a variety of fancy-coloured diamonds... their colours were described as 'jonquil, lemon, aquamarine, sultana-green, gold button, grey, blue, crevet, lilac, rose, old port, madeira and topaz'... as such, the necklace ranked among the most important creations of this century in fancy-coloured diamonds..."
I. Balfour   1987

"... From what cause, therefore, do colours arise in Nature? It is nothing but the disposition of bodies to reflect the rays of a certain order and to absorb all the rest..."

François Voltaire   1734

Number 41
Weight .... 0.47 ct
Measurements .... 6.41 x 4.20 x 2.65 mm
Shape .... oval
Cutting .... modern brilliant
Common Name .... brass
Hue (HUE) .... brown-yellow (BR-Y)
Lightness (LIT) .... medium (Med)
Saturation (SAT) .... strong (St)

"... Where there is a sensuous delight, like that of colour, and the impression of the object is in its elements agreeable, we have to look no farther for an explanation of the charm we feel..."

G. Santayana   1896

Number 42
Weight .... 0.49 ct
Measurements .... 6.28 x 4.35 x 2.56 mm
Shape .... oval
Cutting .... modern brilliant
Common Name .... old rose
Hue (HUE) .... brownish pink (br-PK)
Lightness (LIT) .... light-medium (Lt-Md)
Saturation (SAT) .... weak (Wk)

"... Collectors lucky enough to own the occasional orange stone whose hue truly conjures pumpkin... know they possess one of the world's rarest diamond treasures. There are just enough of these stones to nourish dreams of owning one. But reality nearly always falls short of fantasy..."

D. Federman   1991

Number 43
Weight .... 0.49 ct
Measurements .... 6.29 x 4.39 x 2.71 mm
Shape .... oval
Cutting .... modern brilliant
Common Name .... pumpkin
Hue (HUE) .... yellow-orange (Y-O)
Lightness (LIT) .... medium (Med)
Saturation (SAT) ....
.... strong-very strong (St-VSt)

"... individual brown diamonds vary widely and can have overtones reflecting a spectrum of colors from green to mahogany..."

A. Langerman   1990
(see Sielaff 1990)

Number 44
Weight .... 0.49 ct
Measurements .... 5.07 - 5.12 x 3.04 mm
Shape .... round
Cutting .... modern brilliant
Common Name .... mahogany
Hue (HUE) .... orangish brown (o-BR)
Lightness (LIT) .... very dark (VDk)
Saturation (SAT) .... weak-moderate (Wk-Md)

Number 45
Weight .... 0.49 ct
Measurements .... 5.08 - 5.17 x 3.07 mm
Shape .... round
Cutting .... modern brilliant
Common Name .... **sapphire**
Hue (HUE) .... blue (B)
Lightness (LIT) .... dark (Dk)
Saturation (SAT) .... weak (Wk)

"... Diamonds of a faint bluish tinge are not unfrequently found... the rich deep blue diamond is of extreme rarity... although writers describe these stones as possessing in an eminent degree the beauty of fine sapphires, no comparison can really be instituted, their blue color being peculiar to themselves — dark, verging on indigo, possessing a characteristic intensity which differs materially from the mild, soft hue of the sapphire..."

E.W. Streeter   1884

"... The Jagersfontein mine is... characterized by... exquisite fancy stones of deep sapphire-blue colour."

P.A. Wagner   1914

Number 46
Weight .... 0.49 ct
Measurements .... 5.11 - 5.14 x 3.07 mm
Shape .... round
Cutting .... modern brilliant
Common Name .... **ochre**
Hue (HUE) ....
.... brownish orangish yellow (br-o-Y)
Lightness (LIT) .... medium (Med)
Saturation (SAT) ... strong-very strong (St-VSt)

"... Coloured diamonds... fine deep golden yellow or canaries and pronounced fancy colours always find a ready market..."

M.D. Rothschild   1891

"... The deep yellow canary diamonds, the black, and brown, and many other shades are also unusual and desirable."

Marcus & Co.   1937

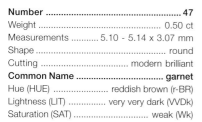

Number 47
Weight .... 0.50 ct
Measurements .... 5.10 - 5.14 x 3.07 mm
Shape .... round
Cutting .... modern brilliant
Common Name .... **garnet**
Hue (HUE) .... reddish brown (r-BR)
Lightness (LIT) .... very very dark (VVDk)
Saturation (SAT) .... weak (Wk)

"... The princely collection of the late Mr. Hope possessed a diamond of a blood-red garnet shade..."

A.C. Hamlin   1884

"... diamonds of strong, rich, deep tints are extremely rare; so, too, are the garnet, hyacinth, rose, peach-blossom, and lilac colored specimens..."

G. Merrill   1922

Number 48
Weight .... 0.50 ct
Measurements .... 6.04 x 4.39 x 2.77 mm
Shape .... pear
Cutting .... modern brilliant
Common Name .... **cinnamon**
Hue (HUE) ....
.... pinkish orangish brown (pk-o-BR)
Lightness (LIT) .... medium (Med)
Saturation (SAT) ...... weak-moderate (Wk-Md)

"... Diamonds occur in all shades, from deep yellow to pure white and jet black, from deep brown to light cinnamon, also green, blue, pink, yellow, orange, and opaque..."

W. Crookes   1909

"... the Kimberley Mine... characterized by yielding brown stones... a considerable percentage of smoky and... Diamonds of a peculiar pinkish brown colour."

P.A. Wagner   1914

"... A large diamond... of a brown colour, with a reflection of a vinous [wine coloured] tinge."

J.L. Bournon 1815

"... 'Fancies' include all decided colors... various shades of blue, rose, copper... are included in this classification..."

W.R. Cattelle 1903

Number	49
Weight	0.51 ct
Measurements	5.15 - 5.17 x 3.14 mm
Shape	round
Cutting	modern brilliant
Common Name	**copper**
Hue (HUE)	orangish pink-brown (o-PK-BR)
Lightness (LIT)	medium-dark (Md-Dk)
Saturation (SAT)	weak-moderate (Wk-Md)

"... However, brown-orange stones, 'burnt orange,' in trade terms, have increased in popularity in recent months..."

R. Shor 1987

Number	50
Weight	0.51 ct
Measurements	5.08 - 5.20 x 3.09 mm
Shape	round
Cutting	modern brilliant
Common Name	**burnt**
Hue (HUE)	brown-orange (BR-O)
Lightness (LIT)	dark (Dk)
Saturation (SAT)	moderate (Mod)

"... There are many different colors — red, green, and blue, probably being the rarest colors. Then there is pink, mauve, violet, orange, all the colors found in the spectrum and many others in combination with each other. Their rarity is such that collectors and connoisseurs are prepared to pay a very high price for these stones..."

J. Roux 1985

Number	51
Weight	0.51 ct
Measurements	5.61 x 4.63 x 2.78 mm
Shape	oval
Cutting	modern brilliant
Common Name	**marigold**
Hue (HUE)	brownish yellow-orange (br-Y-O)
Lightness (LIT)	medium (Med)
Saturation (SAT)	very strong (VSt)

"... Colors speak all languages..."

Joseph Addison 1714

"... 'Canaries' whose bright yellow is faintly highlighted by a hint of orange."

C. Crespin 1984

Number	52
Weight	0.51 ct
Measurements	5.04 - 5.08 x 3.26 mm
Shape	round
Cutting	modern brilliant
Common Name	**sunflower**
Hue (HUE)	orangish yellow (o-Y)
Lightness (LIT)	medium (Med)
Saturation (SAT)	
	strong-very strong (St-VSt)

Number 53
Weight .... 0.51 ct
Measurements .... 6.19 x 4.26 x 2.85 mm
Shape .... pear
Cutting .... modern brilliant
Common Name .... **saffron**
Hue (HUE) .... orange-yellow (O-Y)
Lightness (LIT) .... light-medium (Lt-Md)
Saturation (SAT) .... strong (St)

"... mix yellow and vermilion, and you will have a saffron or gold colour."

T. Nicols   1652

"... Yes, I answered you last night, No, this morning, Sir, I say, Colors seen by candlelight will not look the same by day..."

Robert Browning   1869

Number 54
Weight .... 0.51 ct
Measurements .... 6.28 x 4.12 x 2.26 mm
Shape .... elongated cushion
Cutting .... antique brilliant
Common Name .... **coral**
Hue (HUE) ....
.... brownish orangish pink (br-o-PK)
Lightness (LIT) .... light (Lt)
Saturation (SAT) .... weak (Wk)

"... the coloured diamond is valuable... according to the glorious beauty of its perfection... it feeds your eyes with much pleasure in beholding, and hence are discovered to us the excellencies of super-celestial things..."

T. Nicols   1652

Number 55
Weight .... 0.52 ct
Measurements .... 6.88 x 4.19 x 2.73 mm
Shape .... pear
Cutting .... modern brilliant
Common Name .... **kunzite**
Hue (HUE) .... pink (PK)
Lightness (LIT) .... light-medium (Lt-Md)
Saturation (SAT) .... weak (Wk)

"... The show-piece amongst a number of 'highly important jewels' sold by auction at Sotheby's on 17th March [1960], was undoubtedly a large pink diamond, cut as an oval brilliant... The stone weighs 34.64 carats, and it has a pleasing shade of pink — not unlike that of kunzite..."

B.W. Anderson   1960

Number 56
Weight .... 0.52 ct
Measurements .... 5.05 - 5.11 x 3.24 mm
Shape .... round
Cutting .... modern brilliant
Common Name .... **amber**
Hue (HUE) ...... brown-orange-yellow (BR-O-Y)
Lightness (LIT) .... medium (Med)
Saturation (SAT) .... moderate-strong (Md-St)

"... A somewhat different coloration, amber-yellow, sometimes with an orange or brownish tinge, distributed throughout the crystal, is found in diamonds..."

Y.L. Orlov   1977

"... They are beautiful to behold, and a critical discussion of them would seem at first to be pendantic [overprecise]... The fact is, however, the color of a diamond is one of the most controversial subjects in the gem world. Sometimes you can turn peaceful, good-humored men of the trade into raging gladiators by asking the simple question — What, precisely, is the perfect color of a diamond?"

J.R. McCarthy   1942

Number	**57**
Weight	0.52 ct
Measurements	5.11 - 5.16 x 3.24 mm
Shape	round
Cutting	modern brilliant
Common Name	**rust**
Hue (HUE)	orange-brown (O-BR)
Lightness (LIT)	dark (Dk)
Saturation (SAT)	moderate (Mod)

"... There are six kinds of diamonds — the Indian diamond, the Arabian, the Macedonian, the Cyprian, the Cenchron and the Siderites... The Cyprian, so called from being found in Cyprus, verges into the colour of brass..."

Pliny   77 A.D.

"... Diamond... gem variety... colourless and pale shades of pink, blue, yellow, green and brown..."

R. Webster   1943

Number	**58**
Weight	0.52 ct
Measurements	6.77 x 4.55 x 2.77 mm
Shape	pear
Cutting	modern brilliant
Common Name	**brass**
Hue (HUE)	greenish brownish yellow (g-br-Y)
Lightness (LIT)	light-medium (Lt-Md)
Saturation (SAT)	moderate-strong (Md-St)

"... Color provokes a psychic vibration. Color hides a power still unknown but real, which acts on every part of the body..."

Wassily Kandinsky   1912

"... Although popularly considered as white or colorless stones, diamonds are found in nearly all the colors of the rainbow... Decided yellow stones are quite rare, but the public generally want white stones, though connoisseurs want the colored."

G.F. Kunz   1927

Number	**59**
Weight	0.52 ct
Measurements	4.74 x 4.67 x 2.65 mm
Shape	square
Cutting	emerald
Common Name	**chartreuse**
Hue (HUE)	greenish yellow (g-Y)
Lightness (LIT)	very light (VLt)
Saturation (SAT)	moderate (Mod)

"... mix a white and a red and you will have a rose colour."

T. Nicols   1652

"... 'Gem color' is at once recognized by those who have seen it before, and usually the uninformed will prefer it above all others, simply on its merits..."

W.R. Cattelle   1911

Number	**60**
Weight	0.53 ct
Measurements	5.30 x 4.96 x 3.20 mm
Shape	cushion-triangle
Cutting	modern brilliant
Common Name	**rose**
Hue (HUE)	purplish pink (pp-PK)
Lightness (LIT)	light-medium (Lt-Md)
Saturation (SAT)	weak-moderate (Wk-Md)

Number 61
Weight .... 0.53 ct
Measurements .... 5.73 x 4.88 x 2.72 mm
Shape .... cushion-oval
Cutting .... modern brilliant
Common Name .... **mauve**
Hue (HUE) .... pink-purple (PK-PP)
Lightness (LIT) .... light (Lt)
Saturation (SAT) .... weak (Wk)

"... a mauve coloured laminated stone of about a carat. It is without exception the finest specimen of its kind yet detected..."
J.R. Sutton   1928

"... The different shades range from pale pink to purple, and may also display tones bestowing on them the qualifiers mauve or lavender."
C. Crespin   1984

Number 62
Weight .... 0.53 ct
Measurements .... 6.01 x 4.33 x 2.87 mm
Shape .... elongated octagon
Cutting .... modified brilliant
Common Name .... **ruby**
Hue (HUE) .... purplish red-pink (pp-R-PK)
Lightness (LIT) .... medium-dark (Md-Dk)
Saturation (SAT) .... moderate (Mod)

"... there are many Rose-colored Diamonds, but the Blood or Ruby Red specimen... — a gem on fire as it were — is unique in all modern experience..."
E.W. Streeter   1884

"... The red varieties of this mineral are rarely of deep tints, but when they exhibit a decided red color they form the most gorgeous of gems..."
A.C. Hamlin   1884

Number 63
Weight .... 0.54 ct
Measurements .... 6.13 x 4.50 x 3.21 mm
Shape .... pear
Cutting .... modern brilliant
Common Name .... **amber**
Hue (HUE) ....
.... orangish brown-yellow (o-BR-Y)
Lightness (LIT) .... medium (Med)
Saturation (SAT) .... strong (St)

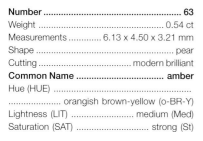

"... The yellow diamond, perhaps, affords the greatest number of shades, some of them surpassing in beauty every other gem of this color."
S.M. Burnham   1886

"... four different yellow diamonds — a canary yellow, a deep cape yellow, an amber yellow and a treated [artificially coloured] yellow."
G.S. Woods   1986

Number 64
Weight .... 0.55 ct
Measurements .... 5.21 - 5.26 x 3.24 mm
Shape .... round
Cutting .... modern brilliant
Common Name .... **chameleon**
Hue (HUE) .... olive (OL)
Lightness (LIT) .... medium-dark (Md-Dk)
Saturation (SAT) .... weak-moderate (Wk-Md)

"... there are diamonds of a sapphire hue, and one of a ruby red... there are also green, white, olive, black, yellow and fire-coloured; but the red and blue are the rarest of all natural productions..."
E.W. Streeter   1882

"... In long wave ultraviolet radiation... the Chameleon Diamond emits a strong, slightly (i.e., turbid) [chalky] yellow luminescence... detailed examination reveals that this emission is slightly uneven..."
E. Fritsch   1995
(see Content 1995)

"... Perhaps the most striking color change of a diamond is in the so-called chameleon... these diamonds appear to be fancy yellow before changing on exposure to light to the dull yellow or gray-green [olive] usually associated with chameleon diamonds... a particularly attractive chameleon stone displayed strong yellow fluorescence and phosphorescence..."

C. Fryer   1982

Number	65
Weight	0.55 ct
Measurements	6.16 x 5.02 x 2.62 mm
Shape	cushion
Cutting	modern brilliant
Common Name	**drab**
Hue (HUE)	brownish yellowish olive (br-y-OL)
Lightness (LIT)	medium (Med)
Saturation (SAT)	moderate (Mod)

"... the term Cape has been synonymous with yellow for more than ninty years... the man most instrumental for the enshrinement of Cape as a synonym for yellow in diamond lexicons was pioneering British gemologist Basil Anderson. During extensive spectroscopic studies of yellowish and yellow diamonds... Anderson noted a correlation between the strength of light absorption bands in the blue and violet regions of the visible spectrum and the strength of color observed. To underscore this relationship, he dubbed these signature absorption bands as 'Cape lines' in 1942... By the end of the decade, all diamonds with such absorption lines were known as 'Cape series' stones..."

D. Federman   1993

Number	66
Weight	0.56 ct
Measurements	7.13 x 4.20 x 3.04 mm
Shape	marquise
Cutting	modern brilliant
Common Name	**lemon**
Hue (HUE)	yellow (Y)
Lightness (LIT)	light (Lt)
Saturation (SAT)	moderate-strong (Md-St)

"... Several specimens occur of reddish shades, such as garnet, hyacynth, lilac, and peach-blossom, seen in the different collections of Europe."

S.M. Burnham   1886

"... Diamonds strongly tinged with color are termed 'fancy' stones, and command their price. Once in a blue moon there is one with color so pronounced as closely to resemble the gem it mimics..."

H. Bridgman   1916

Number	67
Weight	0.57 ct
Measurements	7.37 x 4.46 x 2.93 mm
Shape	marquise
Cutting	modern brilliant
Common Name	**garnet**
Hue (HUE)	orangish reddish brown (o-r-BR)
Lightness (LIT)	very dark (VDk)
Saturation (SAT)	weak-moderate (Wk-Md)

"... the habit [external shape] of some... amber-coloured fancies, is identical with that of typical Wesselton diamonds."

P.A. Wagner   1914

"... Of all colored diamonds, yellows are the most familiar. The majority come from South Africa and range in color from a pale lemon souffle to the color of an amber warning light..."

D. Kaye   1986

Number	68
Weight	0.57 ct
Measurements	5.12 - 5.21 x 3.42 mm
Shape	round
Cutting	modern brilliant
Common Name	**amber**
Hue (HUE)	brown-orange-yellow (BR-O-Y)
Lightness (LIT)	medium (Med)
Saturation (SAT)	moderate-strong (Md-St)

Number 69
Weight .... 0.57 ct
Measurements .... 5.43 - 5.49 x 3.22 mm
Shape .... round
Cutting .... modern brilliant
Common Name .... **leek**
Hue (HUE) .... olive (OL)
Lightness (LIT) .... medium-dark (Md-Dk)
Saturation (SAT) .... weak (Wk)

"... Those diamonds which show true green body color are quite rare, but a number of stones showing olive green have been found in the Finsch Mine in South Africa..."

G. Tombs   1980

Number 70
Weight .... 0.57 ct
Measurements .... 4.99 - 5.18 x 3.47 mm
Shape .... round
Cutting .... modern brilliant
Common Name .... **old orchid**
Hue (HUE) .... brownish purple (br-PP)
Lightness (LIT) .... light-medium (Lt-Md)
Saturation (SAT) .... weak-moderate (Wk-Md)

"... Some diamonds show a smokey-brown color reminiscent of smoky quartz; others are mauve [purple], similar to pale amethyst. These colors are not infrequently found mixed, some parts of the crystals showing a mauve color and the remainder varying intensities of a smoky hue..."

Y.L. Orlov   1977

Number 71
Weight .... 0.58 ct
Measurements .... 5.48 - 5.54 x 3.20 mm
Shape .... round
Cutting .... modern brilliant
Common Name .... **moss**
Hue (HUE) ...... brownish green-olive (br-G-OL)
Lightness (LIT) .... medium-dark (Md-Dk)
Saturation (SAT) .... moderate (Mod)

"... colored diamonds... they are extremely rare and in very, very high demand... Most such stones are sold at top auctions or brokered to private collectors; prices in the six figures are very common... they are quite literally collectors items. This means that once the stones are sold they go into collections, never to be seen again until the estate sale..."

R. Shor   1987

Number 72
Weight .... 0.59 ct
Measurements .... 7.82 x 4.28 x 2.84 mm
Shape .... marquise
Cutting .... modern brilliant
Common Name .... **autumn**
Hue (HUE) ....
.... brownish yellowish orange (br-y-O)
Lightness (LIT) .... medium-dark (Md-Dk)
Saturation (SAT) .... strong (St)

"... The international gemstone marketplace, however, recognizes the great rarity and beauty of fancy diamonds. This recognition takes the form of demand/supply inequities, resulting in a single fact: Top quality fancy diamonds are the most expensive of all gemstones... They are a market unto themselves; continued demand and a vanishingly small supply have made these gems terribly expensive... the prices of fancy diamonds have continued to rise..."

J. Arem   1982

"... to Kings alone the sages assigned two classes of colored diamonds, — namely, those red as coral and those yellow as saffron. These were exclusively royal gems, but diamonds of all other shades could be set in royal jewels..."

L. Finot   1896

Number 73
Weight .... 0.59 ct
Measurements .... 4.87 x 4.69 x 2.99 mm
Shape .... square-octagon
Cutting .... modified brilliant
Common Name .... **saffron**
Hue (HUE) .... orange-yellow (O-Y)
Lightness (LIT) .... light (Lt)
Saturation (SAT) .... strong (St)

"... Although pure diamond is one of the simplest of materials chemically [pure carbon], very frequently a small amount of [nitrogen] impurity is included and it is this which is largely responsible for giving so many diamonds a yellowish tinge... Of the delicately coloured transparencies, which can fetch very high prices, there occur, occasionally, canary-yellows..."

S. Tolansky   1962

Number 74
Weight .... 0.59 ct
Measurements .... 5.58 x 4.31 x 3.05 mm
Shape .... rectangle-octagon
Cutting .... modified brilliant
Common Name .... **daffodil**
Hue (HUE) .... yellow (Y)
Lightness (LIT) .... light (Lt)
Saturation (SAT) .... strong (St)

"... when you see a diamond actually change from one distinct colour to another... such was the case... of a 2.02 carat brilliant-cut diamond... there before me lay a brilliant yellow stone!... but its colour started to change through various shades of yellow and yellow/green until it was back to the [olive] colour it was the night before. These so called 'chameleon' diamonds... change from green [olive] to yellow... the change has been variously described as being associated either with changes in temperature or in the amount of light reaching the stone..."

K. Scarratt   1984

Number 75
Weight .... 0.60 ct
Measurements .... 7.18 x 4.62 x 2.96 mm
Shape .... pear
Cutting .... modern brilliant
Common Name .... **chameleon**
Hue (HUE) .... olive (OL)
Lightness (LIT) .... dark (Dk)
Saturation (SAT) .... weak-moderate (Wk-Md)

"... success in preserving the color and enhancing the brilliancy of many fancy diamonds by cutting them entirely 'brilliant'... right proportions and exact facetings has... raised them in the scale of beauty by cutting, and shown that some of the finer specimens of the cheaper varieties may be made to rival in beauty others far more costly..."

W.R. Cattelle   1903

Number 76
Weight .... 0.60 ct
Measurements .... 8.81 x 4.30 x 2.89 mm
Shape .... marquise
Cutting .... modern brilliant
Common Name .... **pewter**
Hue (HUE) .... gray (GY)
Lightness (LIT) .... medium (Med)
Saturation (SAT) .... weak (Wk)

Number 77
Weight .... 0.61 ct
Measurements .... 6.04 x 4.33 x 3.22 mm
Shape .... oval
Cutting .... modern brilliant
Common Name .... chartreuse
Hue (HUE) .... green-yellow (G-Y)
Lightness (LIT) .... very light (VLt)
Saturation (SAT) ..... strong-very strong (St-VSt)

"... the existence of Brazilian diamonds... with a colour very similar to that of the yellowish-green of uranium glass, but inclining more to yellow..."

E. Boutan   1886

Number 78
Weight .... 0.61 ct
Measurements .... 7.05 x 5.04 x 2.66 mm
Shape .... pear
Cutting .... modern brilliant
Common Name .... cinnamon
Hue (HUE) ....
.... pinkish orangish brown (pk-o-BR)
Lightness (LIT) .... medium-dark (Md-Dk)
Saturation (SAT) .... moderate (Mod)

"... Premier mine... cleavage fragments of cinnamon brown colour are greatly in evidence."

P.A. Wagner   1914

"Cinnamon, brown, black, milky, and opalescent diamonds are occasionally met with..."

G. Merrill   1922

Number 79
Weight .... 0.61 ct
Measurements .... 9.06 x 4.37 x 2.67 mm
Shape .... marquise
Cutting .... modern brilliant
Common Name .... cornflower
Hue (HUE) .... grayish blue (gy-B)
Lightness (LIT) .... light-medium (Lt-Md)
Saturation (SAT) .... weak (Wk)

"... Premier mine... there are occasionally found cleavage fragments of exquisite sky-blue colour, the like of which is seen in no other mine."

P.A. Wagner   1914

"... the natural blue diamonds vary from steel blue, to light cornflower blue and, very occasionally... pure blue..."

T. Loevy   1981

Number 80
Weight .... 0.61 ct
Measurements .... 5.04 x 6.52 x 2.83 mm
Shape .... heart
Cutting .... modern brilliant
Common Name .... thistle
Hue (HUE) .... pink-purple (PK-PP)
Lightness (LIT) .... light-medium (Lt-Md)
Saturation (SAT) .... weak-moderate (Wk-Md)

"... absolute perfection is no more to be found in Diamonds and Precious Stones, than in any other created thing; for, however perfect they may appear, there is, as a rule, some trifling defect... among the most frequent defects are: Feathers — fissures inside the stone..."

E.W. Streeter   1884

"... the facts of life for most orange diamonds. Orange and brown are more apt to be paired in nature than orange and yellow. Given this reality, the trade should re-evaluate hardened attitudes toward brown-orange diamonds..."

D. Federman   1991

Number 81
Weight .... 0.62 ct
Measurements .... 6.47 x 4.89 x 3.05 mm
Shape .... oval
Cutting .... modern brilliant
Common Name .... cognac
Hue (HUE) ....
.... yellowish brown-orange (y-BR-O)
Lightness (LIT) .... medium-dark (Md-Dk)
Saturation (SAT) .... strong (St)

"... The astonishing fact about a diamond is that its beauty is largely due to the bending of a line of light, not to its appearance, as the Lord made it — 'scarcely more impressive,' as King Edward remarked of the Great Cullinan, when shown to him in the rough, 'than a glassy pebble kicked aside in the road.' From a curiosity this is converted into a thing of beauty by the skill of the cutter to catch the light and, by means of many facets, at exactly the right angle, every step calculated to a nicety, to send it back and forth, like battledore and shuttlecock, till wearied with the struggle it is allowed to rest at last in its lover's eye..."

H. Bridgman   1916

Number 82
Weight .... 0.62 ct
Measurements .... 5.42 - 5.50 x 3.30 mm
Shape .... round
Cutting .... modern brilliant
Common Name .... khaki
Hue (HUE) .... brown-olive-yellow (BR-OL-Y)
Lightness (LIT) .... medium-dark (Md-Dk)
Saturation (SAT) .... moderate (Mod)

"... the precious crystals of the Vaal river beds are exceptionally good... some are lightly tinged with yellow, detracting somewhat from their market value, but there was a large percentage of stones perfectly white, or so nearly colorless as to defy any scrutiny except that of experts... Deep orange-yellow stones were occasionally found, and all shades of yellow grading to the finest straw color were represented as well as pale blue, brown, and pink, and other hues; but any color except white [colorless] or yellow is rarely to be seen..."

G.F. Williams   1905

Number 83
Weight .... 0.62 ct
Measurements .... 7.89 x 4.53 x 2.97 mm
Shape .... marquise
Cutting .... modern brilliant
Common Name .... saffron
Hue (HUE) .... orange-yellow (O-Y)
Lightness (LIT) .... light-medium (Lt-Md)
Saturation (SAT) ..... strong-very strong (St-VSt)

"... The green-tinted diamonds... as stones of this character rarely weigh much over ¹/₂ carat and are usually smaller. A few are of sufficiently deep colour to be classed as fancies. They are a light apple-green similar to the Willemite [variety of serpentine]..."

W.R. Cattelle   1911

"... Since 1985, only a very few diamonds with green color certified as natural have been sold at auction. One of the most notable: a 3.02 carat 'apple-green' which sold for $564,000 per carat at Sotheby's in April 1988..."

D. Federman   1990

Number 84
Weight .... 0.62 ct
Measurements .... 5.03 - 5.17 x 3.78 mm
Shape .... round
Cutting .... antique brilliant
Common Name .... apple
Hue (HUE) .... yellowish green (y-G)
Lightness (LIT) .... light-medium (Lt-Md)
Saturation (SAT) .... weak-moderate (Wk-Md)

Number 85
Weight .... 0.63 ct
Measurements .... 7.34 x 4.67 x 2.71 mm
Shape .... oval
Cutting .... modern brilliant
Common Name .... cocoa
Hue (HUE) .... brown (BR)
Lightness (LIT) .... medium (Med)
Saturation (SAT) .... weak-moderate (Wk-Md)

"... The relatively few brown stones with decidedly more body color — enough to qualify them as colored stones — are eligible for... fancy color designations: 'fancy light' (ginger-ale colored), 'fancy' (milk chocolate) or 'fancy dark' (dark coffee)... the term fancy before brown helps to reduce, often remove, the stigma of being brown..."
D. Federman   1988

Number 86
Weight .... 0.63 ct
Measurements .... 7.53 x 4.59 x 2.45 mm
Shape .... pear
Cutting .... antique brilliant
Common Name .... bottle
Hue (HUE) .... green (G)
Lightness (LIT) .... medium (Med)
Saturation (SAT) .... weak-moderate (Wk-Md)

"... Perfect stones of decided green form the most magnificent gems of this colour..."
A.C. Hamlin   1884

"... green coloration in diamond crystals... In some deposits one finds ordinary transparent crystals with a uniform bottle-green coloration... Green transparent diamonds with the color extending throughout the crystal are found relatively rarely..."
Y.L. Orlov   1977

Number 87
Weight .... 0.63 ct
Measurements .... 7.39 x 4.06 x 3.32 mm
Shape .... marquise
Cutting .... modern brilliant
Common Name .... hydrangea
Hue (HUE) .... grayish blue (gy-B)
Lightness (LIT) .... medium (Med)
Saturation (SAT) .... weak (Wk)

"... the pretty diamond of twenty carats with five facets and the colour of hydrangeas which Tavernier had procured..."
E. Steingräber   1968

"... Only very recently has the diamond market begun to accept fancy grayish Blue diamonds on equal terms with unmodified fancy blues... Changing attitudes toward fancy grayish Blue diamonds may have been forced on dealers and collectors by the marked shortage of true-blue stones in recent years..."
D. Federman   1990

Number 88
Weight .... 0.63 ct
Measurements .... 5.82 x 5.06 x 3.62 mm
Shape .... modified pear
Cutting .... modern brilliant
Common Name .... amethyst
Hue (HUE) .... pinkish purple (pk-PP)
Lightness (LIT) .... medium (Med)
Saturation (SAT) .... weak-moderate (Wk-Md)

"... Diamonds usually classified as colorless actually show various pale shades of color; these are usually referred to as 'off-color' in trade circles. Apart from such colorless diamonds, there are crystals having a weak but quite definite coloration, and also deeply colored in various shades of yellow, green, brown, pink, and mauve 'amethystine,' dark blue, milk-white, gray and black..."
Y.L. Orlov   1977

"... Blue diamonds are usually of very pale bluish... tint. A few deeper blue stones are seen occasionally as 'fancy' diamonds. These are seldom as deep blue as pale sapphires...some of the deeper blue diamonds have a steely cast..."

F.B. Wade   1918

"... The color ranges from a pale sky blue, passing through steel blue, to a dark, inky blue."

E.J. Gübelin   1980

Number	**89**
Weight	0.63 ct
Measurements	7.15 x 5.10 x 2.97 mm
Shape	pear
Cutting	modern brilliant
Common Name	**steel**
Hue (HUE)	gray-blue (GY-B)
Lightness (LIT)	medium-dark (Md-Dk)
Saturation (SAT)	weak (Wk)

"... Grey diamond... Probably much the most frequent of all. The colour range is entirely in grey, excepting for some slight amount of overlapping into other species [colour varieties]..."

J.R. Sutton   1928

Number	**90**
Weight	0.64 ct
Measurements	10.01 x 4.12 x 2.69 mm
Shape	marquise
Cutting	modern brilliant
Common Name	**ash**
Hue (HUE)	whitish gray (wh-GY)
Lightness (LIT)	light (Lt)
Saturation (SAT)	weak (Wk)

"... It is, however, somewhat remarkable that this gem, although possessing several shades of color, never, or very rarely, occurs of a decided violet or purple colour..."

A.C. Hamlin   1884

"... the aim of the cutter... is to develop the best color contained in the crystal... as it is seldom equally distributed... color often lies in strata, blotches, or sections of the rough stone..."

W.R. Cattelle   1903

Number	**91**
Weight	0.64 ct
Measurements	9.10 x 4.66 x 2.63 mm
Shape	marquise
Cutting	modern brilliant
Common Name	**lavender**
Hue (HUE)	purple (PP)
Lightness (LIT)	very light (VLt)
Saturation (SAT)	weak (Wk)

"... In spring, there is the young, tender, green wheat and the pink apple blossom... summer is characterized by the contrast of blue skies with golden orange wheat... in autumn, there is the contrast of the yellow leaves with the violet tones of decay... in winter, there is snow with little black figures..."

Vincent van Gogh   1882

"... Below this, forming the centre of the ornament, is a round pink Brazilian brilliant of 9 ¹¹/₁₆ carats, described as a good and rare stone."

L. Twining   1960

Number	**92**
Weight	0.64 ct
Measurements	5.58 - 5.64 x 3.34 mm
Shape	round
Cutting	modern brilliant
Common Name	**blossom**
Hue (HUE)	pink (PK)
Lightness (LIT)	light (Lt)
Saturation (SAT)	weak (Wk)

Number 93	
Weight .... 0.64 ct	
Measurements .... 7.27 x 4.54 x 2.98 mm	
Shape .... marquise	
Cutting .... modern brilliant	
Common Name .... chrome	
Hue (HUE) .... orangish yellow (o-Y)	
Lightness (LIT) .... light-medium (Lt-Md)	
Saturation (SAT) .... very strong (VSt)	

"... The orange-yellow diamonds are always on the small side, and in the majority of instances of very irregular habit [shape]. Occasional chrome-yellow cubes... belong to this species..."

J.R. Sutton   1928

Number 94	
Weight .... 0.65 ct	
Measurements .... 6.88 x 4.73 x 3.27 mm	
Shape .... pear	
Cutting .... modern brilliant	
Common Name .... ochre	
Hue (HUE)	
.... brownish orangish yellow (br-o-Y)	
Lightness (LIT) .... light-medium (Lt-Md)	
Saturation (SAT) ... strong-very strong (St-VSt)	

"... The colour which occurs most frequently in diamonds is yellow, in various shades, such as citron-yellow, wine-yellow, brass-yellow, ochre-yellow, and honey-yellow..."

M. Bauer   1904

Number 95	
Weight .... 0.65 ct	
Measurements .... 6.06 x 4.43 x 2.78 mm	
Shape .... rectangle	
Cutting .... emerald	
Common Name .... chartreuse	
Hue (HUE) .... greenish yellow (g-Y)	
Lightness (LIT) .... very light (VLt)	
Saturation (SAT) .... strong (St)	

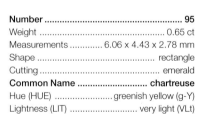

"... There is another item of importance, though it escapes general observation. It is the quality of color. In fancies, the hues being deep, it is more noticeable and therefore regarded. A fine canary is of a clean bright yellow like the feathers of the bird after which it is named. Frequently the yellow is tainted by a greenish [chartreuse] cast... Absinthe-green diamonds are sometimes very beautiful... stones of this color are apt to have an oily appearance [due to fluorescence]... occasionally these stones show wide variations of color under different lights..."

W.R. Cattelle   1911

Number 96	
Weight .... 0.65 ct	
Measurements .... 6.09 x 4.40 x 2.77 mm	
Shape .... rectangle	
Cutting .... emerald	
Common Name .... chartreuse	
Hue (HUE) .... greenish yellow (g-Y)	
Lightness (LIT) .... very light (VLt)	
Saturation (SAT) .... strong (St)	

"... Most of the yellow diamonds are coloured with one or other... tints... green is the most commonly occurring colour, especially in Brazilian diamonds..."

M. Bauer   1904

"... The true shade in all gems is that degree of natural color most pleasing to the eye... It should affect the sense of sight as silk velvet feels to the touch — rich and soft... No gem color is harsh or thin or watery..."

W.R. Cattelle   1911

Number	97
Weight	0.65 ct
Measurements	5.41 - 5.50 x 3.49 mm
Shape	round
Cutting	modern brilliant
Common Name	**moss**
Hue (HUE)	olive (OL)
Lightness (LIT)	medium-dark (Md-Dk)
Saturation (SAT)	weak (Wk)

"... The most beautiful colored diamonds combine a host of rare qualities."

C. Crespin   1984

"... Pink diamonds lacking the 'pure' hue are politely classified as 'collectors items,' for the buyer who wishes to add them to a cabinet of curiosities..."

P. Proddow   1994

Number	98
Weight	0.65 ct
Measurements	7.15 x 4.40 x 3.29 mm
Shape	marquise
Cutting	modern brilliant
Common Name	**rouge**
Hue (HUE)	orangish brown-pink (o-BR-PK)
Lightness (LIT)	medium (Med)
Saturation (SAT)	weak-moderate (Wk-Md)

"... the only specimen known to jewellers... it passed ultimately into the possession of a great connoisseur... for richness of color it may not inaptly be likened to an African sunset..."

E.W. Streeter   1884

Number	99
Weight	0.65 ct
Measurements	8.29 x 4.38 x 2.84 mm
Shape	marquise
Cutting	modern brilliant
Common Name	**sherry**
Hue (HUE)	
	orangish reddish brownish pink (o-r-br-PK)
Lightness (LIT)	medium-dark (Md-Dk)
Saturation (SAT)	weak-moderate (Wk-Md)

"... There is a ruby red diamond that has proved of great interest to the members of the trade, as well as several gems of gold, orange, pistache green, and other hues, that were far from the color that is ordinarily credited to crystalline carbon."

A. Eknayan   1904

"... The love of precious stones is deeply implanted in the human heart, and the cause of this must be sought... in their coloring and brilliancy..."

G.F. Kunz   1913

Number	100
Weight	0.66 ct
Measurements	5.81 x 6.67 x 3.08 mm
Shape	heart
Cutting	modern brilliant
Common Name	**marigold**
Hue (HUE)	yellow-orange (Y-O)
Lightness (LIT)	medium (Med)
Saturation (SAT)	very strong (VSt)

Number	101
Weight	0.66 ct
Measurements	5.46 - 5.55 x 3.50 mm
Shape	round
Cutting	modern brilliant
Common Name	**bronze**
Hue (HUE)	olivish yellow-brown (ol-Y-BR)
Lightness (LIT)	dark (Dk)
Saturation (SAT)	moderate (Mod)

"... in colored diamonds... their tints and shades are so peculiar and varied that they may better be described individually than in groups..."

E.W. Streeter   1884

Number	102
Weight	0.66 ct
Measurements	5.13 x 4.65 x 3.29 mm
Shape	rectangle
Cutting	emerald
Common Name	**sunflower**
Hue (HUE)	brownish orangish yellow (br-o-Y)
Lightness (LIT)	medium (Med)
Saturation (SAT)	very strong (VSt)

"... The product of DeBeers Mine... dodecahedral fancy stones of a characteristic deep yellow colour."

P.A. Wagner   1914

"... It is not difficult to tell if a stone is cut to the best proportion. If when held both near and far, it seems full of light and life, it has fulfilled its destiny..."

H. Bridgman   1916

Number	103
Weight	0.66 ct
Measurements	6.90 x 4.84 x 2.77 mm
Shape	oval
Cutting	modern brilliant
Common Name	**chartreuse**
Hue (HUE)	green-yellow (G-Y)
Lightness (LIT)	very light (VLt)
Saturation (SAT)	moderate-strong (Md-St)

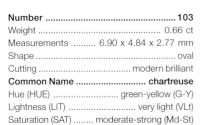

"... Brazilian diamonds... show the characteristic luminescence and greenish yellow color of some of the Bahian diamonds."

O.C. Farrington   1934

"... Whereas diamonds in their natural state show all colours of the rainbow, such as blue-white, distinctly blue, bottle-green, light green, yellow, green-yellow, pink and brown..."

J.F.H. Custers   1956

Number	104
Weight	0.67 ct
Measurements	5.66 x 4.40 x 3.20 mm
Shape	rectangle-octagon
Cutting	modified brilliant
Common Name	**chocolate**
Hue (HUE)	brown (BR)
Lightness (LIT)	medium (Med)
Saturation (SAT)	weak-moderate (Wk-Md)

"... The Kimberley West and Paardeberg East mines, situated to the west of Kimberley, yielded... a considerable proportion of brilliant brown stones."

P.A. Wagner   1914

"... The most beautiful of these colors range from a medium brown to a dark chocolate, the latter being not only most desirable, but very difficult to find. I daresay that it is easier to find more D-E-F colors than pure chocolate brown diamonds!... desirable brown diamonds are far rarer than commonly imagined..."

H. Harris   1990

"... all diamonds of pronounced and pleasing color are called 'fancy' diamonds in the trade. Certain of these 'fancy' diamonds are still further defined by using a name specifying the color, as, for example, 'canary' diamonds (when of a fine bright yellow)."

F.B. Wade   1916

"... Canary, the shade familiar to most people, is a yellow of deep intensity... the appellation 'canary' is, however, often used indiscriminately. A true 'canary' is so rare..."

D. Kaye   1986

Number	105
Weight	0.67 ct
Measurements	5.58 - 5.62 x 3.48 mm
Shape	round
Cutting	modern brilliant
Common Name	**canary**
Hue (HUE)	yellow (Y)
Lightness (LIT)	light (Lt)
Saturation (SAT)	strong (St)

"... Amid the crash of music and the booming of guns, the sultan Abu Bakar of Jehore [Malaysia] took his seat on one of the gilded chairs on the dais with the British governor on his left. Around his highness' neck was a collar of diamonds and in the decorations that covered his breast were diamonds, emeralds, and rubies of almost priceless value. Each button of his coat and low-cut vest was a diamond... in one of his buttonholes blazed a diamond orchid..."

Rounseville Wildman   1891
(see Brus 1987)

"... the rarest diamonds are those which are distinctly colored stones such as orange, deep blue, red, pink, orchid, and green."

Marcus & Co.   1937

Number	106
Weight	0.68 ct
Measurements	6.66 x 5.11 x 2.96 mm
Shape	oval
Cutting	modern brilliant
Common Name	**orchid**
Hue (HUE)	purple (PP)
Lightness (LIT)	light-medium (Lt-Md)
Saturation (SAT)	weak-moderate (Wk-Md)

"... besides the 'Hope' and 'Brunswick' diamonds, there are only three diamonds known in Europe that can justly be termed 'blue,' and these all differ from the 'Hope' and from each other in colour..."

E.W. Streeter   1882

"... Deeply colored stones [diamonds] are more common than in most fields: reds [pink], blues, smoky [brown] stones, and black occurring."

S.H. Ball   1931

Number	107
Weight	0.68 ct
Measurements	7.60 x 4.83 x 2.91 mm
Shape	pear
Cutting	modern brilliant
Common Name	**bluebird**
Hue (HUE)	grayish blue (gy-B)
Lightness (LIT)	light-medium (Lt-Md)
Saturation (SAT)	weak (Wk)

"... Perhaps the most characteristic and at the same time unusual feature of all Rand and Klerksdorp [South African] diamonds is that they are almost invariably green — light-green, dark-green or olive-green..."

E. Rosenthal   1950

Number	108
Weight	0.68 ct
Measurements	9.08 x 5.07 x 2.34 mm
Shape	marquise
Cutting	modern brilliant
Common Name	**laurel**
Hue (HUE)	olivish green (ol-G)
Lightness (LIT)	medium (Med)
Saturation (SAT)	weak-moderate (Wk-Md)

Number 109
Weight .... 0.68 ct
Measurements .... 6.16 x 4.53 x 3.44 mm
Shape .... oval
Cutting .... modern brilliant
Common Name .... chrome
Hue (HUE) .... orangish yellow (o-Y)
Lightness (LIT) .... light-medium (Lt-Md)
Saturation (SAT) .... very strong (VSt)

"... Yellow diamonds are found in abundance, Canary diamonds almost never."

C. Crespin   1984

"... A colored diamond is a touchstone of the universe, a little something God created that man can't always find... they are the last frontier of collectables..."

R. Winston   1986
(see Kaye 1986)

Number 110
Weight .... 0.69 ct
Measurements .... 5.29 - 5.37 x 3.64 mm
Shape .... round
Cutting .... modern brilliant
Common Name .... lettuce
Hue (HUE) .... yellow-green (Y-G)
Lightness (LIT) .... light (Lt)
Saturation (SAT) .... moderate (Mod)

"... color in green diamonds is thought to result from natural irradiation in the earth — most likely after the stones' formation. According to current theory, some time in a diamond's history it comes into contact with a mineral containing radioactive elements such as uranium whose high-energy particles create defects in the diamond's atomic structure... these radiation-induced defects are, in turn, responsible for the absorption of wavelengths of red light by the diamond that result in the transmission of a complimentary green color to the eye..."

D. Federman   1990

Number 111
Weight .... 0.69 ct
Measurements .... 5.46 x 4.65 x 3.38 mm
Shape .... cushion
Cutting .... antique brilliant
Common Name .... oil
Hue (HUE) ..... greenish brown-yellow (g-BR-Y)
Lightness (LIT) .... medium (Med)
Saturation (SAT) .... very strong (VSt)

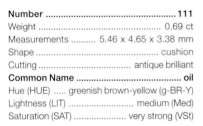

"... In point of color it is one of the most remarkable stones in the whole collection — a gem as it is — being really of the color of crude petroleum, deep yellowish brown. And what is still more remarkable, the stone is as fluorescent as that substance. A gem cut from this stone would be very beautiful."

G.F. Kunz   1885

"... some diamonds... can easily be recognized by a peculiar double colour, a curious combination of yellow and blue or brown and green, which in many cases has an oily appearance... this double colour has to be seen to be understood, but the shading seen in oil probably best describes it..."

A. Monnickendam   1955

Number 112
Weight .... 0.69 ct
Measurements .... 5.49 x 7.05 x 2.81 mm
Shape .... heart
Cutting .... modern brilliant
Common Name .... honey
Hue (HUE) ....
.... orangish brownish yellow (o-br-Y)
Lightness (LIT) .... light-medium (Lt-Md)
Saturation (SAT) .... strong (St)

"... diamond crystals are mostly transparent and somewhat colorless; and not unfrequently they are tinged garnet-red, hyacinth-red, or honey-yellow..."

E.W. Streeter   1884

"... The commonest shades found are honey-yellow, though other shades of yellow are frequently found, except sulfur-yellow."

W. Goodchild   1908

"... in 'fancy' stones... sometimes various shades of color appear in the same stone... by skillful manipulation bad shades of color are neutralized or modified... by judicious cutting..."

W.R. Cattelle   1903

Number 113
Weight .... 0.70 ct
Measurements .... 8.27 x 4.48 x 3.09 mm
Shape .... marquise
Cutting .... modern brilliant
Common Name .... autumn
Hue (HUE) ....
.... yellowish brown-orange (y-BR-O)
Lightness (LIT) .... medium-dark (Md-Dk)
Saturation (SAT) .... strong (St)

"... Most brown diamonds and some white and other coloured diamonds show glide planes [graining] to a very marked degree. This gives the stone the appearance of being badly cracked and shattered. The test has never failed, and on every occasion when I have shown an old digger a stone of this description I have received the same reply: 'A stone like that is very liable to fall to pieces'... My experience over many years proves most conclusively that very few diamonds explode, or fly into pieces after they reach the sorting table..."

A.F. Williams   1932

Number 114
Weight .... 0.71 ct
Measurements .... 8.56 x 4.44 x 3.12 mm
Shape .... marquise
Cutting .... modern brilliant
Common Name .... khaki
Hue (HUE) ..... yellowish olive-brown (y-OL-BR)
Lightness (LIT) .... medium (Med)
Saturation (SAT) .... moderate (Mod)

"... In the diamond trade they are called 'fancies', the rare stones of well-marked colors. They may be red, pea green, apple green, rose, violet-blue, pale sapphire blue, absinthe green, golden brown, orange, yellow, and every color and combination of colors extant..."

J.R. McCarthy   1942

"... These stones, whose array of colors remind dealers of an 'autumn hillside,' combine yellow and orange with brown..."

D. Federman   1983

Number 115
Weight .... 0.72 ct
Measurements .... 5.06 x 6.18 x 3.73 mm
Shape .... heart
Cutting .... modern brilliant
Common Name .... autumn
Hue (HUE) ....
.... yellowish brownish orange (y-br-O)
Lightness (LIT) .... medium-dark (Md-Dk)
Saturation (SAT) .... strong (St)

"... All the colors of flowers and foliage and even the blue sky and the glory of the sunset clouds, only last for a short time, and are subject to continual change, but the sheen and coloration of precious stones are the same to-day as they were thousands of years ago and will be for thousands of years to come. In a world of change, this permanence has a charm of its own that was early appreciated..."

G.F. Kunz   1913

Number 116
Weight .... 0.72 ct
Measurements .... 4.95 x 6.87 x 3.71 mm
Shape .... heart
Cutting .... modern brilliant
Common Name .... sky
Hue (HUE) .... gray-blue (GY-B)
Lightness (LIT) ....light (Lt)
Saturation (SAT) .... weak (Wk)

Number 117
Weight .... 0.72 ct
Measurements .... 8.07 x 4.85 x 2.97 mm
Shape .... marquise
Cutting .... modern brilliant
Common Name .... chameleon
Hue (HUE) .... grayish olive (gy-OL)
Lightness (LIT) .... light-medium (Lt-Md)
Saturation (SAT) .... weak-moderate (Wk-Md)

"... If kept in darkness this colour is retained... should the stone be exposed to diffuse daylight, or to the direct rays of the sun, the change to the original colour is much more rapid..."

M. Bauer   1904

"... A particularly precious variety is the so-called chameleon diamond, which changes color according to the environmental conditions."

E.J. Gübelin   1980

Number 118
Weight .... 0.72 ct
Measurements .... 5.50 - 5.54 x 3.63 mm
Shape .... round
Cutting .... modern brilliant
Common Name .... brick
Hue (HUE) ...... reddish orange-brown (r-O-BR)
Lightness (LIT) .... very dark (VDk)
Saturation (SAT) .... moderate-strong (Md-St)

"... the beauty of the DeBeers' Fancy Collection... one of the rarest ensembles of coloured diamonds in the world, this unique collection of 150 diamonds of all colours of the rainbow... varying in size from half a carat to over two carats, their colors range from pink, green, violet, purple, brick-red, and grey to all the shades of blue..."

Diamond News   1980

"... a 'brick-red' diamond was especially appreciated by fanciers of coloured diamonds..."

B. Zucker   1984

Number 119
Weight .... 0.72 ct
Measurements .... 6.95 x 5.25 x 3.37 mm
Shape .... calf's head
Cutting .... modern step
Common Name .... cognac
Hue (HUE) ....
.... orangish yellowish brown (o-y-BR)
Lightness (LIT) .... medium-dark (Md-Dk)
Saturation (SAT) .... strong (St)

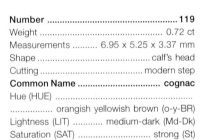

"... Colored diamonds have always been coveted by the elite: By Kings and Queens, sultans and celebrities. One of Queen Elizabeth's favorite brooches, for example, contains a rose [pink] colored diamond, Elizabeth Taylor has a fancy brown, which she calls 'Cognac over ice'..."

H. Huffer   1987

Number 120
Weight .... 0.73 ct
Measurements .... 5.65 - 5.69 x 3.59 mm
Shape .... round
Cutting .... modern brilliant
Common Name .... amber
Hue (HUE) ....
.... yellowish brownish orange (y-br-O)
Lightness (LIT) .... medium (Med)
Saturation (SAT) ...... moderate-strong (Md-St)

"... Diamonds occur in a wide range of colors. The most familiar are basically white or colorless usually with a tinge of yellow or gray. Richly colored stones, called fancies, are rare and highly prized. Fancy colors include golden-yellow, blue, green, pink and amber..."

J. Arem   1975

"... very fine golden-coloured fancy stones are unearthed occasionally, invariably in the form of cleavage [fragments], and hardly ever exceeding two carats each in weight..."

W. Crookes   1909

Number 121
Weight .... 0.73 ct
Measurements .... 7.18 x 5.47 x 3.24 mm
Shape .... pear
Cutting .... modern brilliant
Common Name .... goldenrod
Hue (HUE) ....
.... brownish orangish yellow (br-o-Y)
Lightness (LIT) .... light-medium (Lt-Md)
Saturation (SAT) .... strong (St)

"... the colored Diamonds exhibit their lustre and clearness best when they are cut; especially the yellow ones, which by candle-light, are very brilliant..."

E.W. Streeter   1884

"... diamonds are colored all the way from colorless to pink, yellow, blue, green, orange, gray, amber, brown, violet [purple], red, and of course black."

B. Jones   1979

Number 122
Weight .... 0.73 ct
Measurements .... 7.82 x 5.77 x 2.76 mm
Shape .... pear
Cutting .... modern brilliant
Common Name .... amber
Hue (HUE) .... orangish yellow (o-Y)
Lightness (LIT) .... light (Lt)
Saturation (SAT) .... strong (St)

"... Some very beautiful brown crystals are found... of a rich coffee brown shade."

G.F. Kunz   1885

"... fancy brown diamonds run a rather spectacular gamut of color resemblances to things like cloves, coffee, cinnamon, tobacco, champagne, cognac and chocolate — and are often described in these appealing terms..."

D. Federman   1983

Number 123
Weight .... 0.73 ct
Measurements .... 8.24 x 4.90 x 3.07 mm
Shape .... marquise
Cutting .... modern brilliant
Common Name .... tobacco
Hue (HUE) .... brown (BR)
Lightness (LIT) .... medium (Med)
Saturation (SAT) .... weak-moderate (Wk-Md)

"... The diamond which was initially green [olive] now appears yellow. If this yellow diamond is exposed to sunlight, the ultraviolet light present supplies enough energy for the electron transfer to be reversed, and as a consequence the diamond reverts to its previous condition and changes from yellow back to green almost instantaneously. Truly a chameleon trick, which can be repeated at will..."

F.A. Raal   1982

Number 124
Weight .... 0.73 ct
Measurements .... 5.61 - 5.66 x 3.72 mm
Shape .... round
Cutting .... modern brilliant
Common Name .... avocado
Hue (HUE) .... yellowish olive (y-OL)
Lightness (LIT) .... medium (Med)
Saturation (SAT) .... weak-moderate (Wk-Md)

Number 125
Weight .... 0.73 ct
Measurements .... 8.65 x 4.63 x 2.74 mm
Shape .... pear
Cutting .... modern brilliant
Common Name .... **thistle**
Hue (HUE) .... pink-purple (PK-PP)
Lightness (LIT) .... light-medium (Lt-Md)
Saturation (SAT) .... weak-moderate (Wk-Md)

"... Color in diamonds is the opportunity of many dealers, and the despair of others, for it is very deceptive, and the public is so confident about what it thinks it sees. What it really does see is not always inherent, but is reflected into the stone from the gold in which it is set, or by conditions of the light under which it is seen..."

W.R. Cattelle   1911

Number 126
Weight .... 0.74 ct
Measurements .... 5.86 - 5.90 x 3.51 mm
Shape .... round
Cutting .... modern brilliant
Common Name .... **milk**
Hue (HUE) .... grayish white (gy-WH)
Lightness (LIT) .... very very light (VVLt)
Saturation (SAT) .... weak (Wk)

"... Some of the diamonds which have a slight milky hue, when cut so as to allow the play of light within the stone, present a very beautiful appearance..."

A.C. Hamlin   1884

"... milky and opalescent diamonds are among the rarities..."

J. Wodiska   1909

Number 127
Weight .... 0.74 ct
Measurements .... 6.24 x 4.87 x 3.30 mm
Shape .... oval
Cutting .... modern brilliant
Common Name .... **flesh**
Hue (HUE) .... grayish pink (gy-PK)
Lightness (LIT) .... light-medium (Lt-Md)
Saturation (SAT) .... weak (Wk)

"... a diamond literally flesh-coloured, most limpid, most tender, it scintillated like a star..."

B. Cellini   1568

"... The Diamonds found at Koom [Kalimantan] and elsewhere on the Sarawak river are rarely of very pure water [body colour], and are mostly tinged with yellow. Some that I saw had a decided reddish [pink] tint, a variety much appreciated in the country when the gem is not too small."

O. Beccari   1904

Number 128
Weight .... 0.74 ct
Measurements .... 4.88 x 4.77 x 3.76 mm
Shape .... square
Cutting .... emerald
Common Name .... **forsythia**
Hue (HUE) .... yellow (Y)
Lightness (LIT) .... very light (VLt)
Saturation (SAT) .... strong (St)

"... as for the water [body colour] of the stones, whereas we in Europe make use of day-light to examine the rough stones, the Indians do that in the night-time, setting up a lamp with a large wick in a hole which they make in a wall, by the light of which they judge of the water and cleaness..."

J.B. Tavernier   1676

"... the Cape diamonds are usually of a yellow tinge..."

G.F. Kunz   1889

"... Color... thinks by itself, independently of the object it clothes..."
Charles Baudelaire   1857

"... Diamonds occur in every hue... Blue, Red, Green, White... There are undoubtedly fine specimens not included in this classification; their tints and shades so peculiar and varied that they may be better described individually than in groups."
E.W. Streeter   1884

Number	129
Weight	0.74 ct
Measurements	6.90 x 5.10 x 3.27 mm
Shape	pear
Cutting	modern brilliant
Common Name	**chartreuse**
Hue (HUE)	green-yellow (G-Y)
Lightness (LIT)	very very light (VVLt)
Saturation (SAT)	moderate-strong (Md-St)

"... a diamond... its colour was a very dark brown, and it had a remarkable lustre..."
L. Dieulafait   1874

"... The Kamfersdam Mine [South Africa] yields diamonds of very inferior quality, dark brown being the predominating colour..."
W. Crookes   1909

Number	130
Weight	0.75 ct
Measurements	5.58 - 5.70 x 3.65 mm
Shape	round
Cutting	modern brilliant
Common Name	**chestnut**
Hue (HUE)	orangish brown (o-BR)
Lightness (LIT)	very dark (VDk)
Saturation (SAT)	weak (Wk)

"... In a general way the prices of cut goods in this market to-day may be stated roughly as follows:... Fine Blue Jagers [colourless with fluorescent bluish tinge] and fancy colors are rapidly advancing..."
W.R. Cattelle   1903

Number	131
Weight	0.75 ct
Measurements	6.00 - 6.04 x 3.43 mm
Shape	round
Cutting	modern brilliant
Common Name	**drab**
Hue (HUE)	brown-yellow-olive (BR-Y-OL)
Lightness (LIT)	dark (Dk)
Saturation (SAT)	moderate (Mod)

"... Collectors never stop at one prime stone. They invariably try to accumulate as many examples of different colors and shades as they can. Since such stones are scarce in the first place, this adds to their rarity..."
R. Shor   1987

Number	132
Weight	0.75 ct
Measurements	6.04 - 6.10 x 3.42 mm
Shape	round
Cutting	modern brilliant
Common Name	**drab**
Hue (HUE)	brown-yellow-olive (BR-Y-OL)
Lightness (LIT)	dark (Dk)
Saturation (SAT)	moderate (Mod)

Number 133
Weight .... 0.75 ct
Measurements .... 6.06 - 6.11 x 3.37 mm
Shape .... round
Cutting .... modern brilliant
Common Name .... **sage**
Hue (HUE) .... grayish olive (gy-OL)
Lightness (LIT) .... medium (Med)
Saturation (SAT) .... weak (Wk)

"... colored diamonds... represent a fascinating and compelling 'other world'... they are hard to find, and they are expensive, but those who possess them will no doubt derive great satisfaction in the ownership of something astonishingly beautiful and as rare as any natural substance to be found on this planet..."

J.S. White   1988

Number 134
Weight .... 0.75 ct
Measurements .... 8.00 x 5.00 x 3.24 mm
Shape .... pear
Cutting .... modern brilliant
Common Name .... **flint**
Hue (HUE) .... olivish gray (ol-GY)
Lightness (LIT) .... medium (Med)
Saturation (SAT) .... weak (Wk)

"... diamonds showing a pronounced colouration... almost all the colours of the mineral kingdom may be represented in numerous and varied tints, so that the suite of colours of the diamond is very extensive..."

M. Bauer   1904

Number 135
Weight .... 0.76 ct
Measurements .... 7.24 x 5.67 x 3.38 mm
Shape .... shield
Cutting .... modern step
Common Name .... **mustard**
Hue (HUE) ....
.... brownish orangish yellow (br-o-Y)
Lightness (LIT) .... light-medium (Lt-Md)
Saturation (SAT) .... strong (St)

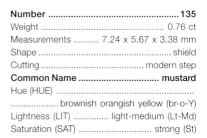

"... Round stones, if their angles are correct, are more brilliant than stones of other contour such as square or cushion shape, or navette [marquise] or heart shape. It can readily be seen that such odd shaped stones can hardly have the same top and back angles at every part of their circumference. Small differences of angle make considerable differences in the brilliancy of cut stones. The prevailing tendency to cut nearly all diamonds round depends largely upon the above facts. In the case of colored diamonds, however, the added attractiveness which comes with odd or different contour more than makes up for the slight loss of brilliancy that may attend upon the shape selected..."

F.B. Wade   1918

Number 136
Weight .... 0.76 ct
Measurements .... 5.59 - 5.62 x 3.75 mm
Shape .... round
Cutting .... modern brilliant
Common Name .... **jade**
Hue (HUE) .... gray-green (GY-G)
Lightness (LIT) .... light (Lt)
Saturation (SAT) .... weak (Wk)

"... Among the treasures of the famous Grünes Gewölbe or 'Green Vaults,' of Dresden, is a celebrated Green Diamond weighing 48 1/2 carats, and valued at £30,000... the visitor who is familiar with the brightly colored [glass] models of this stone... feels some little disappointment on seeing the original, the color of which is the faintest possible shade of green..."

E.W. Streeter   1884

"... In the year 1869 the South Kensington [Victoria and Albert] Museum became possessed of a valuable collection of precious stones... The Townshend collection of precious stones contains 154 specimens, nearly all of them mounted in gold, as rings... coloured diamond is represented in the Townshend Collection by six specimens: black... honey-yellow... pale grayish green... bluish gray... pale indigo blue... pale pinky cinnamon..."

A.H. Church   1913

Number	137
Weight	0.76 ct
Measurements	7.04 x 4.89 x 3.16 mm
Shape	oval
Cutting	modern brilliant
Common Name	**honey**
Hue (HUE)	orangish yellow-brown (o-Y-BR)
Lightness (LIT)	medium (Med)
Saturation (SAT)	moderate-strong (Md-St)

"... The conglomerates of the Witwatersrand [South African] beds, which are probably of pre-Cambrian age, have been found to carry a few diamonds. The colour of these diamonds ranges from cadmium-yellow to yellow-green and dark green..."

A.F. Williams   1932

Number	138
Weight	0.76 ct
Measurements	7.75 x 4.92 x 3.25 mm
Shape	pear
Cutting	modern brilliant
Common Name	**cadmium**
Hue (HUE)	orangish yellow (o-Y)
Lightness (LIT)	light (Lt)
Saturation (SAT)	very strong (VSt)

"... If you feel the mystery of the rainbow, you are drawn by the colored diamond..."

H. Bridgman   1916

"... Gray diamonds are found quite frequently. The gray color is usually due to the presence of numerous microscopic dark inclusions... Depending on the quantity of inclusions, diamonds of these varieties may be clear, [light] gray, dark gray or perfectly black..."

Y.L. Orlov   1977

Number	139
Weight	0.78 ct
Measurements	5.83 - 5.89 x 3.67 mm
Shape	round
Cutting	modern brilliant
Common Name	**nickel**
Hue (HUE)	gray (GY)
Lightness (LIT)	light-medium (Lt-Md)
Saturation (SAT)	weak (Wk)

"... the diamond, like a knight of old — brilliant and resistant, is the emblem of fearlessness and invincibility..."

G.F. Kunz   1913

Number	140
Weight	0.79 ct
Measurements	5.92 - 5.97 x 3.62 mm
Shape	round
Cutting	modern brilliant
Common Name	**nickel**
Hue (HUE)	gray (GY)
Lightness (LIT)	light-medium (Lt-Md)
Saturation (SAT)	weak (Wk)

Number 141
Weight .... 0.79 ct
Measurements .... 7.79 - 5.99 x 3.57 mm
Shape .... modified kite
Cutting .... modern step
Common Name .... buttercup
Hue (HUE) .... orangish yellow (o-Y)
Lightness (LIT) .... light-medium (Lt-Md)
Saturation (SAT) .... very strong (VSt)

"... 'Fancies' include all decided colors, or those having a rare and beautiful tint... a clean buttercup yellow, or an orange yellow, would be 'fancy'..."

W.R. Cattelle   1903

Number 142
Weight .... 0.79 ct
Measurements .... 5.86 - 5.94 x 3.50 mm
Shape .... round
Cutting .... modern brilliant
Common Name .... oil
Hue (HUE) .... olivish yellow (ol-Y)
Lightness (LIT) .... medium (Med)
Saturation (SAT) .... moderate-strong (Md-St)

"... Yellow Diamond... The characteristic tint is near that of olive oil; but the range of color extends all the way from that of a limpid water to deep orange..."

J.R. Sutton   1928

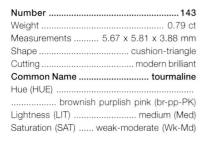

Number 143
Weight .... 0.79 ct
Measurements .... 5.67 x 5.81 x 3.88 mm
Shape .... cushion-triangle
Cutting .... modern brilliant
Common Name .... tourmaline
Hue (HUE) ....
.... brownish purplish pink (br-pp-PK)
Lightness (LIT) .... medium (Med)
Saturation (SAT) ...... weak-moderate (Wk-Md)

"... diamonds occur of every hue... they seem to take pleasure in assuming in turns the colors proper to other gems..."
Jean de Mandeville   ca. 14th century
(see Gill 1978)

"... As the limpid [colourless] or white diamond surpasses all other whiter stones in the power of its lustre and the magnificence of its fire, so do the colored diamonds outrank the emerald, ruby, sapphire, and other gems of like colors."

A.L. Sutton   1894

Number 144
Weight .... 0.79 ct
Measurements .... 5.98 x 5.17 x 3.78 mm
Shape .... oval
Cutting .... modern brilliant
Common Name .... clover
Hue (HUE) .... pink-purple (PK-PP)
Lightness (LIT) .... medium (Med)
Saturation (SAT) .... weak-moderate (Wk-Md)

"... It is necessary, above all things, that a stone of whatever kind, have some positive merit... A crystallized dew-drop that holds the play of the sun will have more lovers, though there is a black spot in the heart of it, than a dead stone which barely winks at high noon, even if perfect..."

H. Bridgman   1916

"... If we were asked: What is the meaning of the words red, blue, black, white, [olive]?, we can of course, immediately point to objects of such-and-such color, but our capicity to explain a meaning of those words does not go far..."

Ludwig Wittgenstein 1931

"... in a box of 'vividly' colored diamonds... one in particular caught my eye... it changed from a gold-yellow to a deep olive green... a rare 'chameleon' diamond..."

D. Landau ca. 1965
(see Harris 1991)

Number	145
Weight	0.80 ct
Measurements	8.29 x 5.61 x 2.88 mm
Shape	pear
Cutting	modern brilliant
Common Name	**chameleon**
Hue (HUE)	olive (OL)
Lightness (LIT)	light-medium (Lt-Md)
Saturation (SAT)	weak (Wk)

"... Of natural yellow diamonds, some show [absorption] bands of the 'Cape' series, while others which are true 'canaries,' show no absorption bands at all and have a yellow fluorescence..."

B.W. Anderson 1943

Number	146
Weight	0.81 ct
Measurements	5.82 - 5.91 x 3.66 mm
Shape	round
Cutting	modern brilliant
Common Name	**maize**
Hue (HUE)	yellow (Y)
Lightness (LIT)	light-medium (Lt-Md)
Saturation (SAT)	strong (St)

"... diamond crystals... yellow-colored... in hue it recalls the color of native sulfur..."

Y.L. Orlov 1977

Number	147
Weight	0.81 ct
Measurements	8.32 x 4.86 x 3.44 mm
Shape	pear
Cutting	modern brilliant
Common Name	**sulfur**
Hue (HUE)	olivish yellow (ol-Y)
Lightness (LIT)	light-medium (Lt-Md)
Saturation (SAT)	strong-very strong (St-VSt)

"... some browns — called cognac, cinnamon, champagne, coffee, chocolate — enjoy a certain esteem..."

C. Crespin 1984

"... a mouth-watering array of lovely brown diamonds... the standard pure-brown diamond, possessing what the trade calls either coffee or chocolate color..."

D. Federman 1988

Number	148
Weight	0.81 ct
Measurements	7.30 x 5.11 x 3.43 mm
Shape	pear
Cutting	modern brilliant
Common Name	**chocolate**
Hue (HUE)	brown (BR)
Lightness (LIT)	medium (Med)
Saturation (SAT)	weak-moderate (Wk-Md)

Number 149
Weight .... 0.82 ct
Measurements .... 5.79 - 5.85 x 3.67 mm
Shape .... round
Cutting .... modern brilliant
Common Name .... amber
Hue (HUE) ....
.... brownish orange-yellow (br-O-Y)
Lightness (LIT) .... medium (Med)
Saturation (SAT) .... very strong (VSt)

"... type Ib diamonds, which are quite rare among natural crystals... are typified by a higher concentration of paramagnetic nitrogen [isolated impurity atoms], which imparts to them an amber-yellow color, and if they also have... yellow luminescence, this may also influence the coloring of the crystal..."

Y.L. Orlov   1977

Number 150
Weight .... 0.82 ct
Measurements .... 6.81 x 4.94 x 3.45 mm
Shape .... oval
Cutting .... modern brilliant
Common Name .... daffodil
Hue (HUE) .... yellow (Y)
Lightness (LIT) .... light (Lt)
Saturation (SAT) .... strong (St)

"... Imagine a gem with the brilliance and dispersion of a diamond... then imagine it in your favorite color of the rainbow. Sound like a dream? Colored diamonds make it reality..."

H. Huffer   1983

Number 151
Weight .... 0.82 ct
Measurements .... 7.53 x 5.36 x 3.56 mm
Shape .... elongated hexagon
Cutting .... modern step
Common Name .... cognac
Hue (HUE) ....
.... orangish yellowish brown (o-y-BR)
Lightness (LIT) .... dark (Dk)
Saturation (SAT) ...... moderate-strong (Md-St)

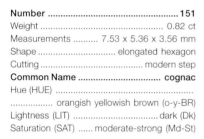

"... surely no pleasure can be more innocent and justifiable than that inspired by the possession of beautiful natural objects..."

G.F. Kunz   1913

"... the deep, pretty shades of the 'fancy' browns."

F.B. Wade   1916

Number 152
Weight .... 0.82 ct
Measurements .... 6.97 x 4.95 x 3.59 mm
Shape .... oval
Cutting .... modern brilliant
Common Name .... hazel
Hue (HUE) .... brown (BR)
Lightness (LIT) .... medium (Med)
Saturation (SAT) .... weak-moderate (Wk-Md)

"... Brown diamonds, more common than others... nevertheless... have a certain subdued charm of their own..."

H. Bridgman   1916

"... Lamination has an intimate correlation with colour. With very few exceptions, all laminated diamonds, no matter where they came from, are coloured — brown, mauve [pink or purple]... slight lamination may also be seen in a way on poor cape-white diamonds, and on poor yellow ones."

J.R. Sutton   1921

"... Scientists have divided diamonds into two groups... Type I and Type II... the later being interesting as natural blue-coloured diamonds are of this type IIb and these stones are electro-conducting..."

R. Webster 1943

Number 153
Weight .... 0.83 ct
Measurements .... 7.49 x 5.12 x 2.82 mm
Shape .... oval
Cutting .... modern brilliant
Common Name .... sky
Hue (HUE) .... bluish gray (b-GY)
Lightness (LIT) .... very light (VLt)
Saturation (SAT) .... weak (Wk)

"... This is an excellent [African] stone of pale brownish golden water [body colour]..."

L. Twining 1960

"... a brown diamond... the gems colour turned out to be a deep, rich golden-brown, with overtones of sienna and burnt orange..."

I. Balfour 1987

Number 154
Weight .... 0.84 ct
Measurements .... 7.44 x 4.54 x 2.71 mm
Shape .... rectangle
Cutting .... emerald
Common Name .... golden
Hue (HUE) ....
.... yellowish orangish brown (y-o-BR)
Lightness (LIT) .... medium (Med)
Saturation (SAT) ...... moderate-strong (Md-St)

"... you can easily understand that such a diamond, particularly because of its unique colour, could be identified anywhere in the world..."

I. Idriess 1948

Number 155
Weight .... 0.84 ct
Measurements .... 8.41 x 4.04 x 3.19 mm
Shape .... marquise
Cutting .... modern brilliant
Common Name .... lavender
Hue (HUE) .... grayish purple (gy-PP)
Lightness (LIT) .... medium (Med)
Saturation (SAT) .... weak (Wk)

"... the least valuable diamonds are those which lack brilliancy, or have faint tints of gray, brown, and yellow. The most prized are those which combine brilliancy with decided tints of rose, green, or blue: cinnamon-coloured, salmon or puce [dark brown] diamonds are also much esteemed..."

A.H. Church 1913

Number 156
Weight .... 0.84 ct
Measurements .... 6.89 x 5.69 x 3.42 mm
Shape .... pear
Cutting .... modern brilliant
Common Name .... rose
Hue (HUE) .... purplish pink (pp-PK)
Lightness (LIT) .... light-medium (Lt-Md)
Saturation (SAT) .... weak-moderate (Wk-Md)

Number 157
Weight .... 0.85 ct
Measurements .... 5.42 x 5.33 x 4.07 mm
Shape .... cushion-round
Cutting .... antique brilliant
Common Name .... chartreuse
Hue (HUE) .... greenish yellow (g-Y)
Lightness (LIT) .... light (Lt)
Saturation (SAT) ..... strong-very strong (St-VSt)

"... I call beautiful that which pleases me at first sight..."
Thomas Aquinas   1267

"... In general, beautifully colored diamonds command fabulous prices and are to be found only in the treasure vaults of princes."
F.B. Wade   1923

Number 158
Weight .... 0.85 ct
Measurements .... 9.34 x 4.91 x 3.19 mm
Shape .... marquise
Cutting .... modern brilliant
Common Name .... absinthe
Hue (HUE) .... yellow-green (Y-G)
Lightness (LIT) .... very light (VLt)
Saturation (SAT) .... moderate (Mod)

"... Absinthe-green diamonds are sometimes very pleasing, though stones of this color are apt to have an oily appearance like some [metamict] zircons..."
W.R. Cattelle   1911

"... Colour is not necessarily detrimental to the value of the diamond as a gemstone. On the contrary, if the diamond still remains transparent and has what one might call a pastel shade of colour, it is very highly prized and the value can be enormously enhanced..."
S. Tolansky   1962

Number 159
Weight .... 0.87 ct
Measurements .... 5.91 - 6.00 x 3.80 mm
Shape .... round
Cutting .... modern brilliant
Common Name .... champagne
Hue (HUE) .... yellowish brown (y-BR)
Lightness (LIT) .... medium (Med)
Saturation (SAT) .... moderate (Mod)

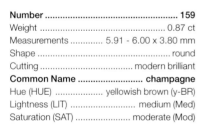

"... Champagne... diamonds seem to be a product of strain in the crystal lattice..."
Argyle Diamonds Ltd.   1989

"... Brown is one of the broadest diamond color families, spanning shades of champagne and ginger-ale, to deep coffee and cognac..."
D. Federman   1991

Number 160
Weight .... 0.88 ct
Measurements .... 6.06 x 4.99 x 3.42 mm
Shape .... rectangle
Cutting .... emerald
Common Name .... golden
Hue (HUE) .... brownish yellow (br-Y)
Lightness (LIT) .... light-medium (Lt-Md)
Saturation (SAT) .... strong (St)

"... Among transparent diamonds of the ordinary variety, one frequently finds crystals with a more or less distinct yellow tinge, or with a clear, golden, straw-yellow color. The coloration is spread throughout the crystal. The entire gamut of shades, showing all gradations from perfectly colorless to deeply colored crystals, can be observed..."
Y.L. Orlov   1977

"... Smoky and brown coloring in diamonds is epigenetic [occurring after the crystal was formed], the initially colorless crystals being so colored by plastic deformation [sheer stress]..."

Y.L. Orlov   1977

Number 161
Weight .... 0.88 ct
Measurements .... 7.24 x 5.85 x 3.35 mm
Shape .... heart
Cutting .... modern brilliant
Common Name .... **walnut**
Hue (HUE) .... yellowish brown (y-BR)
Lightness (LIT) .... medium-dark (Md-Dk)
Saturation (SAT) .... moderate (Mod)

"... the diamond in its purest condition is colorless, and transparent; yet at times it is found colored throughout with pale-yellow, ochre-yellow, light bottle-green, yellowish-green, blackish-green, blue, red, brown, and even black..."

E.W. Streeter   1884

"... golden brown, orange and canary yellow are some of the colors in which diamonds are formed."

F.B. Wade   1923

Number 162
Weight .... 0.89 ct
Measurements .... 5.96 - 6.05 x 3.86 mm
Shape .... round
Cutting .... modern brilliant
Common Name .... **ochre**
Hue (HUE) ....
.... orangish brown-yellow (o-BR-Y)
Lightness (LIT) .... medium-dark (Md-Dk)
Saturation (SAT) ...... moderate-strong (Md-St)

"... in some of its chrome-like tints the diamond is without an equal among the gems..."

A.C. Hamlin   1884

"... Until recently, only shrewd collectors knew that diamonds were available in shades of pink, blue, green, lavender, and canary yellow. When such 'fancies' are fine, they far surpass the value of a top D-rated colorless stone..."

P.D. Lawrence   1980

Number 163
Weight .... 0.89 ct
Measurements .... 6.17 - 6.22 x 3.79 mm
Shape .... round
Cutting .... modern brilliant
Common Name .... **dandelion**
Hue (HUE) .... orangish yellow (o-Y)
Lightness (LIT) .... light-medium (Lt-Md)
Saturation (SAT) ..... strong-very strong (St-VSt)

"... In general, the zircon blues, the tourmaline greens, and the topaz golds of irradiation, either natural or induced, are readily distinguished from pigmented blue, canaries, pinks, and reds. Some stones, however... have a citrine hue essentially like that of irradiated stones..."

F.H. Pough   1988

Number 164
Weight .... 0.89 ct
Measurements .... 6.23 - 6.25 x 3.72 mm
Shape .... round
Cutting .... modern brilliant
Common Name .... citrine
Hue (HUE) .... brownish orange (br-O)
Lightness (LIT) .... dark (Dk)
Saturation (SAT) .... moderate-strong (Md-St)

Number 165
Weight .... 0.90 ct
Measurements .... 10.60 x 4.92 x 3.11 mm
Shape .... marquise
Cutting .... modern brilliant
Common Name .... beige
Hue (HUE) .... yellowish brown (y-BR)
Lightness (LIT) .... light (Lt)
Saturation (SAT) .... weak-moderate (Wk-Md)

"... shade and clarity determine whether yellows and certain very special browns are classified as gems or industrials..."
G.G. Blakey   1977

"... Natural brown diamonds with overtones of pink, red, orange, yellow, or black exhibit unique colors which are referred to in terms such as coffee, cognac, beige, chocolate, and bronze..."
S.C. Hofer   1983

Number 166
Weight .... 0.90 ct
Measurements .... 7.50 x 5.11 x 3.57 mm
Shape .... marquise
Cutting .... modern brilliant
Common Name .... sage
Hue (HUE) .... gray-olive (GY-OL)
Lightness (LIT) .... light-medium (Lt-Md)
Saturation (SAT) .... weak (Wk)

"... Chameleon diamonds typically change reversibly from a gray-green to a brighter yellow color when heated in the flame of an alcohol lamp. Such photochromic behavior was formerly described... in diamonds from the South African gold mines..."
E. Fritsch   1991

Number 167
Weight .... 0.90 ct
Measurements .... 10.56 x 4.69 x 3.01 mm
Shape .... marquise
Cutting .... modern brilliant
Common Name .... teal
Hue (HUE) .... blue-green (B-G)
Lightness (LIT) .... light-medium (Lt-Md)
Saturation (SAT) .... weak (Wk)

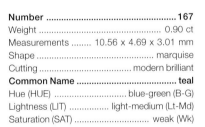

"... we know the Borneo diamonds, like those of the Vaal fields in South Africa, occur in gravel beds from four to six feet thick, on river terraces... Colours vary widely, including yellow, blue-green, brownish-red... and black..."
E. Rosenthal   1950

"... On the east coast of Kalimantan [Borneo] were Sultans of Koetei, who had amassed a vast treasury. In particular, Sultan Aji Moehamad Soelaiman XVII (1850-1899) spent a great deal of his fortune on jewelry and precious stones. His diamond collection contained colored diamonds ranging from yellow to green, grey-blue, and black..."
R. Brus   1987

Number 168
Weight .... 0.91 ct
Measurements .... 5.89 - 5.97 x 3.92 mm
Shape .... round
Cutting .... modern brilliant
Common Name .... corn silk
Hue (HUE) ....
.... greenish brownish yellow (g-br-Y)
Lightness (LIT) .... light (Lt)
Saturation (SAT) .... moderate (Mod)

"... Occasionally these [diamonds] show wide variations of color under different lights; one in New York being absinthe-green... [or] brown... according to the light in which it is seen..."
W.R. Cattelle   1911

"... I love to study the things that grow below the corn stalks and bring them back to my studio to study the color. If one could only catch that true color of nature — the very thought of it drives me mad..."
Andrew Wyeth   1965

"... diamonds ought to be colorless like water; but although they are commonly so, yet from a foreign intermixture [impurity] they are sometimes white, green, yellow, gray, brown, and more rarely red, black, orange, and blue."

J.L. Babe   1872

"... the definite grey diamond, of leaden hue..."

J.R. Sutton   1928

Number 169
Weight .... 0.92 ct
Measurements .... 6.42 x 7.50 x 3.11 mm
Shape .... heart
Cutting .... modern brilliant
Common Name .... lead
Hue (HUE) .... gray (GY)
Lightness (LIT) .... light-medium (Lt-Md)
Saturation (SAT) .... weak (Wk)

"... a large number of the [South African] diamonds are 'off- colored' stones, generally exhibiting a delicate straw-tint, but none the less they are extremely beautiful when properly cut..."

E.W. Streeter   1884

"... Diamond... It is generally colorless, but sometimes tinged with yellow, pink, red, orange, green, blue, brown, or black..."

G.F. Kunz   1918

Number 170
Weight .... 0.92 ct
Measurements .... 10.64 x 4.80 x 3.14 mm
Shape .... marquise
Cutting .... modern brilliant
Common Name .... straw
Hue (HUE) ....
.... orangish brownish yellow (o-br-Y)
Lightness (LIT) .... light (Lt)
Saturation (SAT) .... moderate (Mod)

"... Many diamonds are perfectly isotropic, but some exhibit a double refraction, which was attributed by Brewster to internal strain... the birefringence is often so regular, being indicated by a network of bands inclined at the octahedron angle... that it is evidently connected with the crystalline structure..."

H.A. Miers   1902

"... In the United States in 1941 a campaign was launched to popularize the... brown diamond. The theme was 'Brown Diamonds for Men.' It is too early at this stage to say whether that campaign will succeed... it should..."

J.R. McCarthy   1942

Number 171
Weight .... 0.95 ct
Measurements .... 6.72 x 5.76 x 3.67 mm
Shape .... cushion
Cutting .... modern brilliant
Common Name .... cognac
Hue (HUE) .... orangish brown (o-BR)
Lightness (LIT) .... dark (Dk)
Saturation (SAT) .... moderate-strong (Md-St)

"... only highly skilled... artisans are entrusted with the cutting of colored diamonds... the qualities for which it is so much valued are only fully developed in the hands of the polisher..."

E.W. Streeter   1884

"... Brazilian diamonds... all colors are found, and the rose, wine colored, and blue varieties are much sought for and valued."

T.C. Dawson   1899

Number 172
Weight .... 0.95 ct
Measurements .... 6.00 x 4.72 x 4.01 mm
Shape .... rectangle-octagon
Cutting .... modified brilliant
Common Name .... rose
Hue (HUE) .... purplish pink (pp-PK)
Lightness (LIT) .... medium (Med)
Saturation (SAT) .... weak-moderate (Wk-Md)

Number 173
Weight .... 0.96 ct
Measurements .... 5.76 - 5.80 x 4.26 mm
Shape .... round
Cutting .... modern brilliant
Common Name .... **ink**
Hue (HUE) .... black (BK)
Lightness (LIT) .... very very dark (VVDk)
Saturation (SAT) .... weak (Wk)

"... Black diamonds of great beauty are occasionally supplied by Borneo... These are so adamantine that ordinary Diamond-dust makes not the smallest impression upon them; and they can only be ground or polished by using their own dust..."
E.W. Streeter   1884

"... A black diamond is odd, unique, rare..."
W.R. Cattelle   1911

Number 174
Weight .... 0.96 ct
Measurements .... 6.70 x 7.35 x 3.43 mm
Shape .... heart
Cutting .... modern brilliant
Common Name .... **cape**
Hue (HUE) .... yellow (Y)
Lightness (LIT) .... very light (VLt)
Saturation (SAT) .... moderate (Mod)

"... Cape — a broad range of diamond color grades for stones that show a distinct yellow tint face-up... top silver cape, silver-cape, cape, and dark cape comprise another three-grade system..."
L.L. Copeland   1960

"... Brilliant yellow 'capes' have been a notable feature of South Afican diamonds on world markets..."
A.N. Wilson   1982

Number 175
Weight .... 0.96 ct
Measurements .... 5.90 - 5.99 x 4.15 mm
Shape .... round
Cutting .... modern brilliant
Common Name .... **ochre**
Hue (HUE) ....
.... orangish brownish yellow (o-br-Y)
Lightness (LIT) .... medium (Med)
Saturation (SAT) ... strong-very strong (St-VSt)

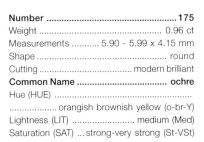

"... it was a round brilliant... and being set in a circle of about a score of white diamonds its tawny complexion was shown to admirable advantage..."
G. Orpen   1890

Number 176
Weight .... 0.98 ct
Measurements .... 9.28 x 5.24 x 3.31 mm
Shape .... oval-marquise
Cutting .... modern brilliant
Common Name .... **cadet**
Hue (HUE) .... bluish gray (b-GY)
Lightness (LIT) .... light-medium (Lt-Md)
Saturation (SAT) .... weak (Wk)

"... Colored diamonds range from yellowish brown to intense brownish orange to greenish gray, pink, yellow, and bluish gray..."
P.D. Lawrence   1980

"... in selecting diamonds... you must mentally ask yourself... Are they like a dew-drop hanging from a damask rose leaf, that is, are they of pure water, and do they possess the power of refraction in a high degree?... of what color?... have they notable imperfections?..."

E.W. Streeter   1884

Number 177
Weight .... 0.98 ct
Measurements .... 7.42 x 6.24 x 3.93 mm
Shape .... heart
Cutting .... modern brilliant
Common Name .... oil
Hue (HUE) .... yellow-olive (Y-OL)
Lightness (LIT) .... light-medium (Lt-Md)
Saturation (SAT) .... moderate (Mod)

"... The diamond is rarely found of a perfect shade of blue..."

A.C. Hamlin   1884

"... There are connoisseurs of blue just as there are connoisseurs of wine..."

Gabrielle Colette   1935

Number 178
Weight .... 0.99 ct
Measurements .... 8.67 x 5.50 x 3.35 mm
Shape .... pear
Cutting .... modern brilliant
Common Name .... cornflower
Hue (HUE) .... blue (B)
Lightness (LIT) .... light-medium (Lt-Md)
Saturation (SAT) .... weak (Wk)

"... the products of each [diamond] mine show differences in either form or colour, which enable an expert readily to recognize their origin... the Wesselton Mine yields a large proportion of flawless octahedra, but, above all, a large number of beautiful deep-orange diamonds..."

G.F.H. Smith   1949

Number 179
Weight .... 1.00 ct
Measurements .... 9.20 x 5.32 x 3.64 mm
Shape .... marquise
Cutting .... modern brilliant
Common Name .... autumn
Hue (HUE) .... brown-orange (BR-O)
Lightness (LIT) .... medium-dark (Md-Dk)
Saturation (SAT) .... strong (St)

"... Diamond is usually transparent, but it may be translucent, and even opaque... even otherwise transparent diamond often contains inclusions which cloud and interupt its clearness... these inclusions may be particles of other materials... or carbonaceous matter..."

O.C. Farrington   1903

"... three [milky] white diamonds displayed what appeared to be a bluish adularescent effect... the adularescent effect was found to result from a combination of extremely minute impurities in the stones, plus bluish fluorescence excited by visible light..."

L.B. Benson   1960

Number 180
Weight .... 1.00 ct
Measurements .... 9.54 x 5.16 x 3.41 mm
Shape .... marquise
Cutting .... modern brilliant
Common Name .... moonstone
Hue (HUE) .... bluish grayish white (b-gy-WH)
Lightness (LIT) .... very very light (VVLt)
Saturation (SAT) .... weak (Wk)

Number 181
Weight .... 1.01 ct
Measurements .... 10.30 x 5.40 x 2.96 mm
Shape .... marquise
Cutting .... modern brilliant
Common Name .... **wheat**
Hue (HUE) ...... olivish brownish yellow (ol-br-Y)
Lightness (LIT) .... light-medium (Lt-Md)
Saturation (SAT) .... moderate-strong (Md-St)

"... The colour of the diamond resembles that of a grain of buckwheat and its appearance is similar to that of fluorspar [i.e., transparent octahedra]. It cuts jade as if it were clay..."

B. Laufer 1915

Number 182
Weight .... 1.01 ct
Measurements .... 7.05 x 5.52 x 3.81 mm
Shape .... oval
Cutting .... modern brilliant
Common Name .... **buttercup**
Hue (HUE) .... orangish yellow (o-Y)
Lightness (LIT) .... light-medium (Lt-Md)
Saturation (SAT) .... very strong (VSt)

"... The number of available colored diamonds is so limited that a small clique of perceptive and affluent dealers and collectors have come to dominate the market. For the most part, the buyers are collectors and the market is a private one, except for the stones sold at public auction..."

J.S. White 1988

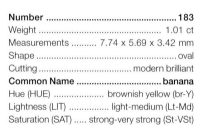

Number 183
Weight .... 1.01 ct
Measurements .... 7.74 x 5.69 x 3.42 mm
Shape .... oval
Cutting .... modern brilliant
Common Name .... **banana**
Hue (HUE) .... brownish yellow (br-Y)
Lightness (LIT) .... light-medium (Lt-Md)
Saturation (SAT) ..... strong-very strong (St-VSt)

"... Rough diamonds occur under the most beautiful and regular geometric forms, their lustre and color frequently resemble gum arabic..."

J. Mawe 1823

"... Most yellow diamonds, however, come from South Africa. It is not too surprising that the term 'Cape series' refers to the Cape of Good Hope and is applied to diamonds with a yellow coloration. The first diamond found in South Africa, the Eureka, is a 10+ carat yellow gem..."

J. Arem 1982

Number 184
Weight .... 1.01 ct
Measurements .... 9.27 x 6.60 x 2.26 mm
Shape .... pear
Cutting .... modern brilliant
Common Name .... **shell**
Hue (HUE) ....
.... orangish brownish pink (o-br-PK)
Lightness (LIT) .... very light (VLt)
Saturation (SAT) .... weak (Wk)

"... An apparently beautiful brilliant, of a pink color, was sent to me, which I estimated at three carats. A great price was asked, and would have been given; but on drawing the gem [removal from its setting] it proved to be lightly tinged with color..."

J. Mawe 1823

"... about five days journey from Golconda, and about half as much again from Bejapoor, there is an extensive plain, where diamonds were found in the 15th and 16th centuries, of great purity and of unusual size... a reddish gray [pink] was visible in the stones..."

E.W. Streeter 1882

"... a number of slaty-colored diamonds are also found which cut very well..."

A.F. Williams 1932

Number 185
Weight .... 1.01 ct
Measurements .... 8.37 x 5.93 x 3.29 mm
Shape .... pear
Cutting .... modern brilliant
Common Name .... slate
Hue (HUE) .... greenish bluish gray (g-b-GY)
Lightness (LIT) .... light-medium (Lt-Md)
Saturation (SAT) .... weak (Wk)

"... All solid and liquid substances absorb light to some extent. If the action be slight and affect uniformly the whole of the visible spectrum, the stone appears to be colorless; if the action [absorption] be greater but still uniform in its effect, the stone appears to be grey..."

G.F.H. Smith 1949

Number 186
Weight .... 1.01 ct
Measurements .... 9.62 x 5.59 x 2.98 mm
Shape .... marquise
Cutting .... modern brilliant
Common Name .... oyster
Hue (HUE) .... gray (GY)
Lightness (LIT) .... light-medium (Lt-Md)
Saturation (SAT) .... weak (Wk)

"... I therefore think it would not be inappropriate to give this substance a definite name, and I propose that of Tiffanyite. It is only the bluish White diamonds... that possess the property of storing up sunlight... and emitting it for a continued period in the dark."

G.F. Kunz 1895

"... Diamonds may be the most perfect reflector of light. It may be purely transparent and colorless as a dewdrop, or it may display all the colors... white, yellow, orange, red, pink, brown, green, blue, black, and opalescent..."

J.W. Hershey 1940

Number 187
Weight .... 1.02 ct
Measurements .... 6.43 - 6.47 x 3.95 mm
Shape .... round
Cutting .... modern brilliant
Common Name .... opalescent
Hue (HUE) ....
.... bluish brownish white (b-br-WH)
Lightness (LIT) .... very very light (VVLt)
Saturation (SAT) .... weak (Wk)

"... Unusually high amounts of hydrogen have been found to be responsible for color in some diamonds... absorption spectrums in the visible range of the bluish and violetish stones were closely related, and appeared to be an 'exaggeration' of the absorption spectrum of the gray stones... violet ones showed a vague [absorption] line at about 590nm in the hand-held spectroscope... researchers concluded these bluish and violetish [gray] diamonds were colored by hydrogen related defects. The exact nature of these defects is unknown..."

E. Fritsch 1991

Number 188
Weight .... 1.02 ct
Measurements .... 8.62 x 5.35 x 3.66 mm
Shape .... pear
Cutting .... modern brilliant
Common Name .... pigeon
Hue (HUE) .... violetish gray (v-GY)
Lightness (LIT) .... medium (Med)
Saturation (SAT) .... weak (Wk)

Number 189
Weight .... 1.02 ct
Measurements .... 6.74 x 5.11 x 2.98 mm
Shape .... rectangle
Cutting .... emerald
Common Name .... seal
Hue (HUE) .... brown (BR)
Lightness (LIT) .... medium-dark (Md-Dk)
Saturation (SAT) .... weak-moderate (Wk-Md)

"... the brown diamond, usually seal or bronze, has little prism play... yet with its lesser brilliance, the brown even in its deepest tints is not without richness, and always exhibits a restlessness, an energy, possessed by no other brown stone..."

H. Bridgman   1916

Number 190
Weight .... 1.03 ct
Measurements .... 8.31 x 5.40 x 3.43 mm
Shape .... oval
Cutting .... modern brilliant
Common Name .... golden
Hue (HUE) .... brownish yellow (br-Y)
Lightness (LIT) .... light-medium (Lt-Md)
Saturation (SAT) .... strong (St)

"... The diamonds from the Kimberley mines have a very wide range of colour — it could almost be said that every conceivable hue is represented in a cross-section of the pipes' yield... yellow, golden yellow, greenish yellow..."

A.N. Wilson   1982

"... Brown is the most common secondary color [modifier] seen in yellow diamonds. The color descriptions for such stones have long enjoyed such fanciful terms as champagne and golden. These terms properly refer to the range of diamond [colour] from slightly brownish Yellow to brownish Yellow up through yellowish Brown..."

S.C. Hofer   1984

Number 191
Weight .... 1.03 ct
Measurements .... 10.07 x 7.01 x 2.02 mm
Shape .... modified kite
Cutting .... antique brilliant
Common Name .... chameleon
Hue (HUE) .... grayish olive (gy-OL)
Lightness (LIT) .... light-medium (Lt-Md)
Saturation (SAT) .... weak (Wk)

"... The greatest value among the objects of human property, not merely among precious stones, is due the adamas [diamond], for a long time known only to Kings, and even to very few of these..."

Pliny   77 A.D.

Number 192
Weight .... 1.04 ct
Measurements .... 6.45 - 6.55 x 3.90 mm
Shape .... round
Cutting .... modern brilliant
Common Name .... buff
Hue (HUE) .... brown (BR)
Lightness (LIT) .... medium (Med)
Saturation (SAT) .... weak-moderate (Wk-Md)

"... the diamond of the Kshatriya should have the brown color of the eye of a hare [jackrabbit]... the Kshatriya diamond prevented the approach of old age..."

L. Finot   1896

"... The diamond... is also known in shades of red, green, and blue, and in brown and black. The two latter are rarely transparent."

O.C. Farrington   1903

"...full bodied yellow stones known as golden fancies, and any other full-bodied colours, such as the very rare deep blues, pinks, and ambers, which are called fancies..."

E. Bruton   1978

"... Notice its symmetry, its color... get your senses involved in the perception of beauty. Let yourself enter into the awareness of beauty... Remove your attention from other things frequently and give a few moments completely to beauty..."

Joyce Kramer   1994

Number	193
Weight	1.05 ct
Measurements	6.29 x 7.79 x 3.74 mm
Shape	heart
Cutting	modern brilliant
Common Name	**goldenrod**
Hue (HUE)	brownish orange-yellow (br-O-Y)
Lightness (LIT)	light-medium (Lt-Md)
Saturation (SAT)	strong-very strong (St-VSt)

"... the old cutters understood... By placing the facets in exact relation to an ideal spot of color they could throw it [colour] around the whole stone, which then faced the spectator as a perfect specimen..."

H. Bridgman   1916

Number	194
Weight	1.05 ct
Measurements	5.76 x 5.26 x 3.60 mm
Shape	square
Cutting	emerald
Common Name	**bubble gum**
Hue (HUE)	purple-pink (PP-PK)
Lightness (LIT)	light-medium (Lt-Md)
Saturation (SAT)	weak-moderate (Wk-Md)

"... The surface of this diamond is coloured by some particles of a green earth, which are incrusted in it."

J.L. Bournon   1815

"... on account of their rarity, there has always been a market, amongst those who can afford such luxuries, for diamonds of decided hue. Of these, yellow 'canary' diamonds and brown 'cinnamon' diamonds are the best known — though even of these perhaps only a few hundred are found in the millions of diamonds mined annually — while few indeed are known which have a pronounced green, blue or red colour..."

B.W. Anderson   1980

Number	195
Weight	1.05 ct
Measurements	5.44 x 5.42 x 4.08 mm
Shape	square-cushion
Cutting	modified brilliant
Common Name	**lettuce**
Hue (HUE)	yellowish green (y-G)
Lightness (LIT)	very light (VLt)
Saturation (SAT)	weak (Wk)

"... The celibrated cabinet of gems belonging to the late Marquis de Dree contained a large and beautiful rose-colored diamond..."

A.C. Hamlin   1884

"... One of the chief pleasures of the diamond owner is to look into its beautiful mysterious depths, from which flash all the colors that ever were..."

H. Bridgman   1916

Number	196
Weight	1.06 ct
Measurements	7.62 x 5.93 x 3.60 mm
Shape	oval
Cutting	modern brilliant
Common Name	**rose**
Hue (HUE)	purplish pink (pp-PK)
Lightness (LIT)	medium (Med)
Saturation (SAT)	moderate (Mod)

```
Number ......................................... 197
Weight ................................... 1.07 ct
Measurements .......... 6.58 - 6.67 x 3.85 mm
Shape ..................................... round
Cutting ..................... modern brilliant
Common Name .............................. buttercup
Hue (HUE) ...................... orangish yellow (o-Y)
Lightness (LIT) ............... light-medium (Lt-Md)
Saturation (SAT) ..... strong-very strong (St-VSt)
```

"... the colored diamond... it is indeed a gem which, for its intrinsic beauty, no less than for its extreme rarity, challenges the foremost place among 'Precious Stones'..."

E.W. Streeter   1884

"... A fine canary is of a clean bright yellow like the feathers of the bird after which it is named..."

W.R. Cattelle   1911

```
Number ......................................... 198
Weight ................................... 1.07 ct
Measurements ........ 10.63 x 5.32 x 3.24 mm
Shape ................................. marquise
Cutting ..................... modern brilliant
Common Name ....................................... rose
Hue (HUE) .......................................... pink (PK)
Lightness (LIT) ............... light-medium (Lt-Md)
Saturation (SAT) ........ weak-moderate (Wk-Md)
```

"... Prince Riccia, of Naples [Italy], acquired in 1830 a very fine rose-colored brilliant of fifteen carats..."

A.C. Hamlin   1884

"... only a few large Pink diamonds have been documented, and their travels through history read like a who's who of merchants, explorers, and royalty... Jean-Baptiste Tavernier (purveyor to Louis XIV)... Harry Winston... Cartier... John Williamson... Mongol emperors... Persian conquerors... Queen Elizabeth II..."

P. Proddow   1994

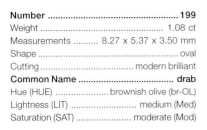

```
Number ......................................... 199
Weight ................................... 1.08 ct
Measurements .......... 8.27 x 5.37 x 3.50 mm
Shape .......................................... oval
Cutting ..................... modern brilliant
Common Name ....................................... drab
Hue (HUE) .................... brownish olive (br-OL)
Lightness (LIT) ......................... medium (Med)
Saturation (SAT) ..................... moderate (Mod)
```

"... Color is often unequally distributed through the stone, or the elements which cause the sensation of color are so placed that position modifies it. There are stones which show more color when viewed from the back than when faced up to the eye. In others it appears deeper when viewed edgewise than in any other direction. Occasionally, the poorest color appears in the the face of the stone, but this is seldom the case, as cutters and cleavers naturally try to arrange their work so that the best color will come to the front in the finished product..."

W.R. Cattelle   1911

```
Number ......................................... 200
Weight ................................... 1.08 ct
Measurements .......... 7.86 x 5.32 x 3.52 mm
Shape .......................................... pear
Cutting ..................... antique brilliant
Common Name ................................... lemon
Hue (HUE) .......................................... yellow (Y)
Lightness (LIT) ........................... very light (VLt)
Saturation (SAT) ........ moderate-strong (Md-St)
```

"... Of the yellow tints, the diamond affords the most beautiful examples, and far surpasses in variety all the other gems..."

A.C. Hamlin   1884

"... the more lemony yellow of a true canary..."

F.H. Pough   1988

"... In the 'Hope Collection' exhibited in 1851, there were three Brilliants [diamonds] of unusual tint — one pink, cushion shaped, the weight of which was 28 carats; the second, lilac-hued, of oval shape, weighing 11 carats; and the third of an apricot color, or a mixture of peach and orange..."

E.W. Streeter　1884

Number 201
Weight .... 1.09 ct
Measurements .... 7.18 x 6.75 x 3.59 mm
Shape .... heart
Cutting .... modern brilliant
Common Name .... lilac
Hue (HUE) .... pinkish purple (pk-PP)
Lightness (LIT) .... medium (Med)
Saturation (SAT) .... weak-moderate (Wk-Md)

"... Of fancy goods [diamonds] the Bulfontein Mine yields stones of a beautiful heliotrope colour."

P.A. Wagner　1914

"... Few fancy colored diamonds were found in the Brazilian diamond mines, and even though South Africa has a large diamond output, her colored diamond production is small, although yellow and orange diamonds have been found in Kimberley and in the Premier Mine, and heliotrope 'light purple' stones have been produced at Bulfontein..."

T. Loevy　1981

Number 202
Weight .... 1.09 ct
Measurements .... 5.81 x 5.56 x 4.13 mm
Shape .... cushion
Cutting .... modern brilliant
Common Name .... heliotrope
Hue (HUE) .... pink-purple (PK-PP)
Lightness (LIT) .... light-medium (Lt-Md)
Saturation (SAT) .... weak-moderate (Wk-Md)

"... Diamond crystals with yellow coloration are extremely common... they are indeed the most abundant colored diamonds... Among transparent diamonds of the ordinary variety, one frequently finds crystals with a more or less distinct yellow tinge, or with a clear, golden, straw-yellow color. The coloration is spread throughout the crystal. The entire gamut of shades, showing all gradations from perfectly colorless crystals to deeply colored crystals, can be observed..."

Y.L. Orlov　1977

Number 203
Weight .... 1.09 ct
Measurements .... 7.57 x 5.93 x 3.77 mm
Shape .... oval
Cutting .... modern brilliant
Common Name .... straw
Hue (HUE) .... yellow (Y)
Lightness (LIT) .... light-medium (Lt-Md)
Saturation (SAT) ..... strong-very strong (St-VSt)

"... many have an educated eye for color and have learned to appreciate the value of good cutting..."

W.R. Cattelle　1903

Number 204
Weight .... 1.09 ct
Measurements .... 8.17 x 5.40 x 3.65 mm
Shape .... oval
Cutting .... modern brilliant
Common Name .... carnelian
Hue (HUE) ....
.... yellowish brown-orange (y-BR-O)
Lightness (LIT) .... medium-dark (Md-Dk)
Saturation (SAT) .... strong (St)

```
Number ..................................... 205
Weight ................................... 1.10 ct
Measurements ........... 6.31 - 6.38 x 4.25 mm
Shape ...................................... round
Cutting .................................... modern brilliant
Common Name ......................................... tan
Hue (HUE) .................... pinkish brown (pk-BR)
Lightness (LIT) ............... light-medium (Lt-Md)
Saturation (SAT) ........ weak-moderate (Wk-Md)
```

"... pink overtones can influence a brown diamond's color... Diamonds of this color have in the past been labeled beige or tan... They are recognized and appreciated as an exceptional [sub] variety of brown diamond..."

S.C. Hofer   1983

```
Number ..................................... 206
Weight ................................... 1.10 ct
Measurements .......... 7.27 x 7.09 x 3.68 mm
Shape ...................................... heart
Cutting .................................... modern brilliant
Common Name ......................................... oil
Hue (HUE) ......................... olivish yellow (ol-Y)
Lightness (LIT) ............... light-medium (Lt-Md)
Saturation (SAT) .............................. strong (St)
```

"... Frequently the yellow is tainted by a greenish cast; many have a dark, murky quality..."

W.R. Cattelle   1911

"... the fascination that a fine set of jewels, with all their sparkle and color, excercises upon the mind... is not only due to the beauty of the spectacle, but is largely owing to the consciousness that they are rare and valuable objects..."

G.F. Kunz   1913

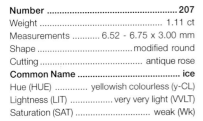

```
Number ..................................... 207
Weight ................................... 1.11 ct
Measurements ........... 6.52 - 6.75 x 3.00 mm
Shape ...................................... modified round
Cutting .................................... antique rose
Common Name ......................................... ice
Hue (HUE) ............. yellowish colourless (y-CL)
Lightness (LIT) ................ very very light (VVLT)
Saturation (SAT) ............................. weak (Wk)
```

"... The name 'Golconda Diamonds' was not derived from the town [fortress] of Golconda near the city of Hyderabad, but was used for the product [i.e., diamonds] obtained from the extensive regions comprised of the provinces watered by the Krishna and Godavari rivers."

S.C. Rudra   1904

"... Colorless... devoid of any color, as is pure water, a pane of ordinary window glass, or a fine diamond; therefore distinctly different from white, as is milk, or white jade... only transparent objects can be colorless... rock crystal is a colorless variety of quartz; milky quartz is a white variety..."

R.M. Shipley   1974

```
Number ..................................... 208
Weight ................................... 1.11 ct
Measurements ........ 10.66 x 5.26 x 3.01 mm
Shape ...................................... marquise
Cutting .................................... modern brilliant
Common Name ......................................... steel
Hue (HUE) ......................... grayish blue (gy-B)
Lightness (LIT) ......................... medium (Med)
Saturation (SAT) ............................. weak (Wk)
```

"... this gem... about the size of a common walnut... had a bluish metallic lustre... of a decided, but rather steel-like blue..."

J. Mawe   1866

"... It is rare when a diamond is vivid blue but there are many beautiful steel blues available to those who love them... I saw one of 18 carats, cut in a pendent [pear] shape, a pool of twilight blue water..."

J.Y. Dickinson   1965

"... Diamonds of all the colors which belong of right to other precious stones are occasionally found... they are red, green, yellow, and blue... the first and last tints being the rarest..."

G. Orpen   1890

"... Among colors of diamonds, blue is the rarest..."

O.C. Farrington   1903

Number	**209**
Weight	1.13 ct
Measurements	8.27 x 5.33 x 4.12 mm
Shape	pear
Cutting	modern brilliant
Common Name	**navy**
Hue (HUE)	blue (B)
Lightness (LIT)	medium-dark (Md-Dk)
Saturation (SAT)	weak-moderate (Wk-Md)

"... on the highest authority... this yellow tinge is a very strong one... almost destroying its brilliancy..."

C.W. King   1867

"... There exist diamonds of all colors. When these are sparkling and clear they augment the value of the stone by reason of their rareness. The colors most frequent are rose, yellow, brown, and orange."

J. Escard   1920

Number	**210**
Weight	1.14 ct
Measurements	9.16 x 5.43 x 4.19 mm
Shape	marquise
Cutting	modern brilliant
Common Name	**lemon**
Hue (HUE)	yellow (Y)
Lightness (LIT)	light (Lt)
Saturation (SAT)	strong (St)

"... Dost thou not see how the artificer Nature delights to represent all things by colors and forms, but more especially in gems?..."

Desiderius Erasmus   1521

"... The various colorings in the diamond have been listed — yellow, golden yellow, deep amber, greenish yellow, orange, brown, cinnamon brown, greenish brown, emerald green, olive green, pale blue, sapphire blue, heliotrope, and red..."

A.N. Wilson   1982

Number	**211**
Weight	1.16 ct
Measurements	6.43 x 5.99 x 4.16 mm
Shape	cushion
Cutting	antique brilliant
Common Name	**amber**
Hue (HUE)	
greenish yellowish brownish orange (g-y-br-O)	
Lightness (LIT)	medium (Med)
Saturation (SAT)	moderate-strong (Md-St)

"... the surface of the native crystal is often rough with little rents [depressions] and flaws, and has a peculiar leaden-grey semi metallic lustre..."

E.W. Streeter   1884

Number	**212**
Weight	1.19 ct
Measurements	11.81 x 6.11 x 2.70 mm
Shape	marquise
Cutting	modern brilliant
Common Name	**lead**
Hue (HUE)	gray (GY)
Lightness (LIT)	light-medium (Lt-Md)
Saturation (SAT)	weak (Wk)

Number 213
Weight .... 1.19 ct
Measurements .... 9.16 x 5.42 x 3.98 mm
Shape .... pear
Cutting .... modern brilliant
Common Name .... cognac
Hue (HUE) ....
.... yellowish orangish brown (y-o-BR)
Lightness (LIT) .... medium-dark (Md-Dk)
Saturation (SAT) ...... moderate-strong (Md-St)

"... The Kimberley West and Paardeberg East mines, situated to the west of Kimberley, yielded... a considerable proportion of brilliant brown stones [diamonds] of distinctive character."

P.A. Wagner   1914

"... Most of these diamonds... he describes alternately as chocolate, golden brown, honey and 'warm'... along with cognac and champagne..."

G. Holmes   1987

Number 214
Weight .... 1.19 ct
Measurements .... 7.51 x 6.05 x 3.75 mm
Shape .... modified shield
Cutting .... modern step
Common Name .... cork
Hue (HUE) .... yellowish brown (y-BR)
Lightness (LIT) .... light-medium (Lt-Md)
Saturation (SAT) .... moderate (Mod)

"... whatever shape... the basic goal is to cut for color. The criteria for a properly cut fancy color diamond are not the same as those for a properly cut white [colourless] stone. The fancy color cutter's objective is to exaggerate rather than mask the appearance of color in the face-up position. Cut characteristics that would be considered detrimental to the beauty of a white diamond — things such as high tops [crowns], thickish girdles, deep backs [pavilions] and unorthodox brilliandeering [final faceting] — might be just the features that transform moderately yellow or brown material into something truely fancy..."

C.A. Meyer   1989

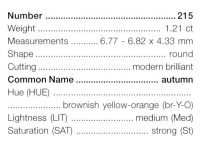

Number 215
Weight .... 1.21 ct
Measurements .... 6.77 - 6.82 x 4.33 mm
Shape .... round
Cutting .... modern brilliant
Common Name .... autumn
Hue (HUE) ....
.... brownish yellow-orange (br-Y-O)
Lightness (LIT) .... medium (Med)
Saturation (SAT) .... strong (St)

"... there was recently offered for sale at public auction... a specimen known as the Orange diamond... which we carefully examined. The [lighting and viewing] circumstance were decidedly adverse to the beauty of a diamond, for it was in the half-light of a London fog that we saw it, yet the stone seemed literally to shoot tongues of yellow fire from its facets... it was a round brilliant..."

G. Orpen   1890

Number 216
Weight .... 1.23 ct
Measurements .... 6.71 - 6.77 x 4.31 mm
Shape .... round
Cutting .... modern brilliant
Common Name .... autumn
Hue (HUE) ....
.... yellowish brownish orange (y-br-O)
Lightness (LIT) .... medium (Med)
Saturation (SAT) ...... moderate-strong (Md-St)

"... a 1-carat brownish orange emerald-cut stone, reminiscent of peak-color autumn foliage, that is among the most beautiful diamonds we have ever seen..."

D. Federman   1988

"... No matter what you call them, brown, amber, coffee, chocolate, champagne, cinnamon, or any other name, this family of diamonds is a family of surprises, both from the standpoint of beauty and price..."

H. Harris   1990

Number	217
Weight	1.29 ct
Measurements	8.53 x 5.49 x 4.19 mm
Shape	pear
Cutting	modern brilliant
Common Name	**khaki**
Hue (HUE)	olivish yellow-brown (ol-Y-BR)
Lightness (LIT)	light-medium (Lt-Md)
Saturation (SAT)	moderate-strong (Md-St)

"... Many Argyle Champagne and Cognacs also exhibit additional hues of yellow or pink..."

G. Brown   1991

"... while there is a reliable supply of champagne diamonds [from the Argyle mine] the product is still rarer than colorless diamonds..."

Argyle Diamonds Ltd.   1992
(see Stephenson 1992)

Number	218
Weight	1.29 ct
Measurements	9.50 x 7.61 x 4.13 mm
Shape	kite
Cutting	modern step
Common Name	**champagne**
Hue (HUE)	yellowish brown (y-BR)
Lightness (LIT)	light-medium (Lt-Md)
Saturation (SAT)	moderate (Mod)

"... The quality of yellow stones varies from a clean, bright yellow to a dark and somewhat muddy shade..."

W.R. Cattelle   1911

"... 'Fancies' flaunt their rainbow colors. Diamonds are far more than colorless gems. Even at premium prices, fancy colored diamonds in almost every hue attract devoted collectors..."

F. Ward   1993

Number	219
Weight	1.30 ct
Measurements	8.83 x 6.13 x 3.72 mm
Shape	oval
Cutting	modern brilliant
Common Name	**manila**
Hue (HUE)	brownish yellow (br-Y)
Lightness (LIT)	light-medium (Lt-Md)
Saturation (SAT)	moderate-strong (Md-St)

"... Crystals with light or dark blue coloration are found relatively rarely in nature. ...these blue diamonds are of type IIb — [containing boron impurities]... they are electrically conductive 'semiconducting'... There is a known case of a diamond half of which was light blue, and the other half colorless..."

Y.L. Orlov   1977

Number	220
Weight	1.32 ct
Measurements	8.66 x 4.64 x 3.29 mm
Shape	rectangle
Cutting	emerald
Common Name	**sky**
Hue (HUE)	blue-gray (B-GY)
Lightness (LIT)	light (Lt)
Saturation (SAT)	weak (Wk)

Number 221
Weight .... 1.32 ct
Measurements .... 9.79 x 5.93 x 3.97 mm
Shape .... pear
Cutting .... modern brilliant
Common Name .... henna
Hue (HUE) ....
.... reddish brownish orange (r-br-O)
Lightness (LIT) .... medium-dark (Md-Dk)
Saturation (SAT) ...... moderate-strong (Md-St)

"... diamonds have also been found near Pretoria [South Africa]; one... is a reddish amber and weighed 1 carat rough, and ¹/₂ carat cut."

G.F. Kunz   1926

"... Orange diamond — a diamond of a distinct orange tint. Many of them are reddish orange-brown, somewhat similar to the color of some zircons. Others are a more vivid reddish-orange color, reminiscent of flame spinel..."

L.L. Copeland   1960

Number 222
Weight .... 1.34 ct
Measurements .... 9.96 x 5.80 x 3.88 mm
Shape .... marquise
Cutting .... modern brilliant
Common Name .... autumn
Hue (HUE) ....
.... yellowish brown-orange (y-BR-O)
Lightness (LIT) .... dark (Dk)
Saturation (SAT) .... strong (St)

"... The public may never find important colored diamonds in their local jewelry store, but most major museums have a few modest-size fancy diamonds on exhibit..."

J.S. White   1988

Number 223
Weight .... 1.34 ct
Measurements .... 8.71 x 6.01 x 3.65 mm
Shape .... oval
Cutting .... modern brilliant
Common Name .... wine
Hue (HUE) .... grayish yellow (gy-Y)
Lightness (LIT) .... light (Lt)
Saturation (SAT) .... weak-moderate (Wk-Md)

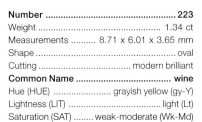

"... The diamond is either colourless or light yellow, passing into wine colour, and then through cinnamon-brown into almost black, also pale-green passing into yellow-green. A dull or faint tinge considerably reduces the value of this gem but when distinctly pink, blue, or green, it is much enhanced and eagerly sought for by connoisseurs..."

J. Mawe   1813

"... most yellow stones appear nearly colorless by artificial light because the excess of yellow rays in the latter makes those from the stone almost invisible..."

O.C. Farrington   1903

Number 224
Weight .... 1.37 ct
Measurements .... 7.39 x 6.48 x 4.22 mm
Shape .... oval
Cutting .... modern brilliant
Common Name .... burnt
Hue (HUE) .... brown-orange (BR-O)
Lightness (LIT) .... very dark (VDk)
Saturation (SAT) .... moderate-strong (Md-St)

"... knowing the exact angle to which rays of light are bent on entering, and the angle at which light endeavoring to pass from a denser medium into the air, as from a diamond, is totally reflected, it has been found possible to so form it and arrange its back facets as to catch the fugitive rays in their effort to pass through, and, by driving them back and forth among the adamantine walls, round them up within the interior and finally return them in brilliant flash-lights through the face of the stone, to the delighted eye of the beholder..."

W.R. Cattelle   1903

"... Grey Diamond... A species of commanding interest. Probably much the most frequent of all. The colour range is entirely in grey, excepting for some slight amount of overlapping into other [colour varieties]... the transparency of the higher grades is nearly perfect... they have a smokey look..."

J.R. Sutton   1928

Number 225
Weight .... 1.39 ct
Measurements .... 7.08 - 7.13 x 4.42 mm
Shape .... round
Cutting .... modern brilliant
Common Name .... taupe
Hue (HUE) .... olivish gray (ol-GY)
Lightness (LIT) .... medium (Med)
Saturation (SAT) .... weak (Wk)

"... Of the other colors in which the diamond occurs, orange... is nevertheless very beautiful..."

W.R. Cattelle   1911

"... Once in a while, you see diamonds of such quality you can't help getting excited about them. I react emotionally to such stones..."

R. Winston   1980
(see Lawrence 1980)

Number 226
Weight .... 1.40 ct
Measurements .... 9.59 x 6.43 x 3.96 mm
Shape .... pear
Cutting .... modern brilliant
Common Name .... citrine
Hue (HUE) ....
.... brownish yellow-orange (br-Y-O)
Lightness (LIT) .... medium (Med)
Saturation (SAT) .... very strong (VSt)

"... Creation plays by very frustrating rules when it comes to pure... orange diamonds. Yet with nearly 100 million carats of diamonds mined annually, collectors of fancy colors still feel good reason to hope for a handful of stones... the search for pure orange diamonds is like looking for a needle in a haystack... to bolster orange in diamonds, nature endows most with brown. This blending is variously described as 'burnt' orange, 'cognac' and 'copper' in the trade..."

D. Federman   1991

Number 227
Weight .... 1.41 ct
Measurements .... 7.24 - 7.27 x 4.23 mm
Shape .... round
Cutting .... modern brilliant
Common Name .... burnt
Hue (HUE) .... brown-orange (BR-O)
Lightness (LIT) .... dark (DK)
Saturation (SAT) .... strong (St)

"... Brazil produces stones of... various shades of coffee..."

H. Pearson   1909

"... Brown and coffee-colored diamonds are not as rare, but are seldom seen in the trade..."

J. Arem   1975

Number 228
Weight .... 1.43 ct
Measurements .... 7.90 x 6.35 x 4.00 mm
Shape .... modified shield
Cutting .... modern step
Common Name .... cafe-au-lait
Hue (HUE) .... brown (BR)
Lightness (LIT) .... light-medium (Lt-Md)
Saturation (SAT) .... weak-moderate (Wk-Md)

Number 229
Weight .... 1.47 ct
Measurements .... 10.45 x 7.06 x 3.46 mm
Shape .... pear
Cutting .... modern brilliant
Common Name .... cape
Hue (HUE) .... yellow (Y)
Lightness (LIT) .... very very light (VVLt)
Saturation (SAT) .... weak-moderate (Wk-Md)

"...Diamonds of yellow color are comparatively common, many of the Cape diamonds... possessing a yellow tinge..."
O.C. Farrington   1903

"... the term 'cape', regularly used in color grading, refers to the yellow tone characteristic of South African diamonds 'Cape of Good Hope'..."
J.O. Gill   1979

Number 230
Weight .... 1.49 ct
Measurements .... 10.07 x 6.60 x 3.63 mm
Shape .... marquise
Cutting .... modern brilliant
Common Name .... drab
Hue (HUE) .... brown-olive (BR-OL)
Lightness (LIT) .... medium (Med)
Saturation (SAT) .... weak-moderate (Wk-Md)

"... Brilliants tinged dull green [olive] or brown are much depreciated by such colors..."
J. Mawe   1823

"... it should be noted that brown and olive are two shades which are not in the spectrum and cannot be matched without the addition of black..."
G.F.H. Smith   1949

Number 231
Weight .... 1.49 ct
Measurements .... 9.70 x 5.36 x 4.68 mm
Shape .... marquise
Cutting .... modern brilliant
Common Name .... cinnamon
Hue (HUE) ....
.... pinkish orangish brown (pk-o-BR)
Lightness (LIT) .... medium-dark (Md-Dk)
Saturation (SAT) .... moderate (Mod)

"... a diamond... of clear cinnamon color, discovered in the Cape [South African] diggings, was pronounced by Diamond merchants of great experience, to be an Indian, and not a Cape stone..."
E.W. Streeter   1884

"... Brown diamonds have a lot going for them. They can be uniquely beautiful and compete with the prettiest fancy colors..."
C.A. Meyer   1992

Number 232
Weight .... 1.50 ct
Measurements .... 7.22 - 7.37 x 4.65 mm
Shape .... round
Cutting .... modern brilliant
Common Name .... mahogany
Hue (HUE) .... orangish brown (o-BR)
Lightness (LIT) .... dark (Dk)
Saturation (SAT) .... weak-moderate (Wk-Md)

"... Diamond, being a cubic mineral, should always show single refraction; but this is not always found to be the case, anomalous double refraction frequently being present, especially in stones that are brown coloured... it is found that many crystals of diamond show signs of great internal strain... this suggests that the mineral is often formed under conditions of great pressure... the brown diamonds from South Africa show the phenomenon in the most marked degree..."
W. Goodchild   1908

"... There are browns coloured exactly like those of the Kimberley zircons, and fragments of brown diamond and zircon are not always to be distinguished apart by eye. Fine fragments of zircon have in fact been taken for diamond by experienced buyers; moreover, fragments of brown diamond have been thrown away as worthless 'Dutch bort' [zircon]... Physical tests can, of course, always determine which is which: among other things the colour can always be taken out of a Kimberley zircon by the flame of a spirit [alcohol] lamp, whereas that of diamond cannot..."

J.R. Sutton   1928

Number	233
Weight	1.53 ct
Measurements	7.11 - 7.21 x 4.61 mm
Shape	round
Cutting	modern brilliant
Common Name	**zircon**
Hue (HUE)	brown (BR)
Lightness (LIT)	medium (Med)
Saturation (SAT)	moderate (Mod)

"... the Grand Duke of Tuscany's diamond, which he has the goodness to show me upon more than one occasion... it weighs 139 1/2 carats, but it is unfortunate that its water [body colour] tends towards the colour of citron..."

J.B. Tavernier   1676

"... Usually the diamond is colorless or white, although shades of yellow are also common..."

O.C. Farrington   1903

Number	234
Weight	1.56 ct
Measurements	8.14 x 5.03 x 4.09 mm
Shape	rectangle
Cutting	emerald
Common Name	**lemon**
Hue (HUE)	yellow (Y)
Lightness (LIT)	very light (VLt)
Saturation (SAT)	moderate (Mod)

"... The more an object is polished or brilliant, the less you see its own color and the more it becomes a mirror reflecting the color of the surroundings..."

Eugené Delacroix   1842

"... About half the diamonds found are tinged to some degree. If the color is but slight, the stone is considered less valuable than if perfectly colorless; but a diamond of pronounced color is the most valuable gem known..."

O.C. Farrington   1903

Number	235
Weight	1.59 ct
Measurements	7.17 x 6.61 x 4.04 mm
Shape	square-octagon
Cutting	modified brilliant
Common Name	**manila**
Hue (HUE)	brown-yellow (BR-Y)
Lightness (LIT)	light-medium (Lt-Md)
Saturation (SAT)	strong (St)

"... the perfect cutting of the diamond is a mathematical problem, governed by rigid laws. All limpid and white [colourless] diamonds must be cut according to this rule, but in case of colored diamonds the case is far different; for perfection of color is to be attained and brilliancy is a secondary thought..."

A.C. Hamlin   1884

"... Diamond cutting is an art, not an industry..."

H. Bridgman   1916

Number	236
Weight	1.64 ct
Measurements	7.73 x 6.83 x 4.56 mm
Shape	modified shield
Cutting	modern step
Common Name	**hazel**
Hue (HUE)	brown (BR)
Lightness (LIT)	medium-dark (Md-Dk)
Saturation (SAT)	moderate (Mod)

Number	237
Weight	1.66 ct
Measurements	6.37 x 6.34 x 4.49 mm
Shape	square-octagon
Cutting	modified brilliant
Common Name	**daffodil**
Hue (HUE)	yellow (Y)
Lightness (LIT)	light (Lt)
Saturation (SAT)	strong (St)

"... Some of the most famous gems in the great collections of the world are fancy diamonds. Among them are some fabulous blue diamonds, including the Hope (45.5 carats), the Wittelsbach (35.5 carats)... the Dresden green (41 carats), the pink Darya-i-nur (176+ carats), the Williamson pink (23.6 carats)... the yellow Tiffany (128.5 carats) and the golden yellow Red Cross diamond (205 carats)..."

E.J. Gübelin   1980

Number	238
Weight	1.68 ct
Measurements	10.00 x 6.51 x 4.15 mm
Shape	pear
Cutting	modern brilliant
Common Name	**champagne**
Hue (HUE)	brown (BR)
Lightness (LIT)	light (Lt)
Saturation (SAT)	weak-moderate (Wk-Md)

"... describe a stone as having a 'champagne,' 'coffee,' or 'cognac' color and suddenly the idea of buying a brown diamond doesn't seem so bad after all..."

D. Federman   1983

"... Champagne Diamonds... are natural color diamonds, one of nature's own precious creations and something to be treasured... The variety of shades of Champagne Diamonds makes for endless combinations and design possibilities..."

Argyle Diamonds Ltd.   1992

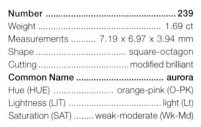

Number	239
Weight	1.69 ct
Measurements	7.19 x 6.97 x 3.94 mm
Shape	square-octagon
Cutting	modified brilliant
Common Name	**aurora**
Hue (HUE)	orange-pink (O-PK)
Lightness (LIT)	light (Lt)
Saturation (SAT)	weak-moderate (Wk-Md)

"... Diamonds are found in many colours, but only when the colours are definite and pleasing do they enhance the value, they are included in the category of fancy stones... sapphire blue, ruby red, pink, canary yellow, green, orange, violet [purple], golden brown are decidedly fancy colours..."

A. Tremayne   1944

"... The beauty of pink diamonds of fine quality is hard to overestimate. The color may vary from a remarkable and fantastic rose pink... to a delicate pale pink that shimmers and glistens... to a peachy-pink or orange-pink reminiscent of some shades of morganite, but utterly dazzling in its brilliance!"

J.A. Henry   1979

Number	240
Weight	1.70 ct
Measurements	7.38 x 5.56 x 4.37 mm
Shape	rectangle
Cutting	emerald
Common Name	**poppy**
Hue (HUE)	brownish orange (br-O)
Lightness (LIT)	dark (Dk)
Saturation (SAT)	strong (St)

"... the beauty of a finished stone depends so much upon the form and position of its facets, that a moderately fine stone, well cut and polished, is of far greater value than a large one less artistically worked..."

E.W. Streeter   1884

"... the deep orange tint is highly valued by collectors for its rarity..."

G.F. Kunz   1889

"... Diamond... limpid, and likewise passing into the greatest variety of shadings from white [colourless] and gray, sometimes from yellow, green, and brown, but more rarely tinged from orange, red, blue, or blackish..."

L. Feuchtwanger   1838

"... Yellow diamonds often contain a light secondary tone of green, brown, or orange..."

J.O. Gill   1979

Number **241**
Weight .... 1.74 ct
Measurements .... 10.37 x 6.36 x 4.32 mm
Shape .... marquise
Cutting .... modern brilliant
Common Name .... **chamois**
Hue (HUE) ....
.... orangish brownish yellow (o-br-Y)
Lightness (LIT) .... light (Lt)
Saturation (SAT) .... moderate (Mod)

"... more particularly the brown stones, show their laminae [graining]..."

J. Mawe   1823

"... We're used in the world to consider the diamond as colourless, but that is an error, as diamonds can be colourless, but they usually offer light shades or tints and sometimes very pronounced colours..."

E. Boutan   1886

Number **242**
Weight .... 1.77 ct
Measurements .... 6.28 x 6.16 x 5.34 mm
Shape .... square
Cutting .... modified brilliant
Common Name .... **walnut**
Hue (HUE) .... yellowish brown (y-BR)
Lightness (LIT) .... medium-dark (Md-Dk)
Saturation (SAT) .... weak-moderate (Wk-Md)

"... diamonds are generally transparent, but they can be translucent and even opaque... jet black..."

E. Boutan   1886

"... At their best, these stones are jet black... totally opaque instead of crystal clear, reflective instead of radiant... what you want from these stones are strong reflections of light off a shiny, polished, completely dark surface. Any area of clear transparency is considered an imperfection... with transparent areas reminiscent of a mirror stripped in places of its backing... there's not much a cutter can do to hide these transparent areas... pitting, as well, is usually unavoidable, a consequence of the fact that black diamonds are incredibly difficult to cut..."

D. Federman   1990

Number **243**
Weight .... 1.83 ct
Measurements .... 7.36 x 6.73 x 5.27 mm
Shape .... oval
Cutting .... modern brilliant
Common Name .... **jet**
Hue (HUE) .... black (BK)
Lightness (LIT) .... very very dark (VVDk)
Saturation (SAT) .... weak (Wk)

"... a diamond containing an inclusion is a source of information... There is also the intrinsic beauty of a diamond that contains an elegantly shaped or coloured mineral inclusion. For example, dark-red, or claret coloured garnets are not uncommon in diamonds and can add character to a polished gem..."

H.O.A. Meyer   1986
(see Gübelin 1986)

Number **244**
Weight .... 1.84 ct
Measurements .... 8.80 x 8.52 x 4.28 mm
Shape .... modified shield
Cutting .... modified brilliant
Common Name .... **chartreuse**
Hue (HUE) .... green-yellow (G-Y)
Lightness (LIT) .... very very light (VVLt)
Saturation (SAT) .... moderate-strong (Md-St)

Number	245
Weight	1.92 ct
Measurements	8.23 - 8.26 x 4.67 mm
Shape	round
Cutting	modern brilliant
Common Name	**sea foam**
Hue (HUE)	bluish gray-green (b-GY-G)
Lightness (LIT)	very light (VLt)
Saturation (SAT)	weak (Wk)

"... We rarely see a green diamond that we feel sure is of natural color. Certainly, in the past 25 years we can recall only one or two dark tourmaline green stones whose history could establish the natural color. Also, each such stone had dark brown to greenish-brown naturals. We have seen several very light almost aquamarine color bluish-green diamonds which we feel are natural in color by virtue of the presence of brown 'stains' in naturals..."

G.R. Crowningshield   1976

Number	246
Weight	2.01 ct
Measurements	9.67 x 6.57 x 4.62 mm
Shape	pear
Cutting	modern brilliant
Common Name	**steel**
Hue (HUE)	blue-gray (B-GY)
Lightness (LIT)	medium (Med)
Saturation (SAT)	weak (Wk)

"... a diamond with the bluish tint of steel... a colouration that affects the entire mass..."

E. Boutan   1886

"... Gems in their appeal are like stars. They enchant the eye, they stir the imagination. Then, as with cats and clocks, they are 'company'..."

H. Bridgman   1916

Number	247
Weight	2.01 ct
Measurements	7.53 - 7.62 x 5.17 mm
Shape	round
Cutting	modern brilliant
Common Name	**hazel**
Hue (HUE)	brown (BR)
Lightness (LIT)	medium (Med)
Saturation (SAT)	weak-moderate (Wk-Md)

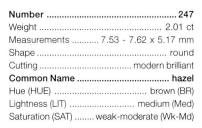

"... getting down to actual color appreciation... certainly some of the fine browns are extremely beautiful... from a strictly appreciative standpoint, however, the beauty of a given color is entirely according to the fancy of the individual. Pronounced colors, though, should not be so deep as to materially affect the brilliancy of the diamond, for above all, the beauty of the gem lies in its unique and gorgeous brilliancy..."

J.C. Fergusson   1927

Number	248
Weight	2.08 ct
Measurements	10.35 x 7.35 x 4.35 mm
Shape	pear
Cutting	modern brilliant
Common Name	**chocolate**
Hue (HUE)	brown (BR)
Lightness (LIT)	medium-dark (Md-Dk)
Saturation (SAT)	moderate (Mod)

"... Most diamond of brown species [variety] is visibly laminated, under magnification if not to the eye. Probably all is laminated, though it may not happen to be manifest, and even where lamination is not seen on the surface, its presence may be indicated by close parallel tinted streaks inside a crystal. Lamination and colour are closely correlated and the darker the brown or mauve [pink or purple] the greater likelihood that the crystal will be laminated in two or in three directions <111> [octahedral] at once..."

J.R. Sutton   1928

"... The diamond crystallizes in the isometric system, and is usually found as an octahedron or some modification of that form... In color, its range is extensive, it having been found in almost every color of the spectrum..."

G.F. Kunz   1890

"... Collectors lucky enough to own the occasional orange stone whose hue truely conjures... cantaloupe know they possess one of the world's rarest diamond treasures... the pure-orange stone... a bonafide pinnacle of diamond beauty..."

D. Federman   1991

Number 249
Weight .... 2.10 ct
Measurements .... 11.68 x 6.34 x 4.54 mm
Shape .... pear
Cutting .... modern brilliant
Common Name .... cantaloupe
Hue (HUE) .... yellowish orange (y-O)
Lightness (LIT) .... light (Lt)
Saturation (SAT) .... strong (St)

"... silver capes or capes, that is white [colourless] stones with a slight yellow tint, are very common, and especially characteristic of the Kimberley mines."

P.A. Wagner   1914

"... The diamond if pure, should contain the element carbon only, but this rarely happens except in the very purest white or colorless crystals... the colour in the diamond may be caused in two ways: by an actual chemical mixture of the element carbon with some other element [e.g., nitrogen, boron, hydrogen] or by minute particles of foreign matter which had been enclosed in the diamond during crystallization..."

A.F. Williams   1932

Number 250
Weight .... 2.11 ct
Measurements .... 7.98 x 7.81 x 4.80 mm
Shape .... cushion
Cutting .... antique brilliant
Common Name .... antique glass
Hue (HUE) .... yellowish colourless (y-CL)
Lightness (LIT) .... very very light (VVLt)
Saturation (SAT) .... weak (Wk)

"... Adamant, or the Diamond, is a most precious Stone, of the Colour of polish'd Iron, and as it were Crystalline..."

Camillus Leonardus   1502

"... After yellow... there are also grey and hyacinthine [orange] diamonds..."

F. Stopford   1920

Number 251
Weight .... 2.12 ct
Measurements .... 11.32 x 6.82 x 4.43 mm
Shape .... pear
Cutting .... modern brilliant
Common Name .... graphite
Hue (HUE) .... gray (GY)
Lightness (LIT) .... medium (Med)
Saturation (SAT) .... weak (Wk)

"... Pure yellow fancy diamonds stretch in intensity from straw through lemon to taxicab yellow..."

D. Federman   1988

Number 252
Weight .... 2.13 ct
Measurements .... 10.01 x 6.94 x 4.78 mm
Shape .... pear
Cutting .... modern brilliant
Common Name .... lemon
Hue (HUE) .... yellow (Y)
Lightness (LIT) .... very light (VLt)
Saturation (SAT) .... moderate-strong (Md-St)

Number 253
Weight .... 2.14 ct
Measurements .... 8.85 x 6.78 x 4.89 mm
Shape .... oval
Cutting .... modern brilliant
Common Name .... canary
Hue (HUE) .... yellow (Y)
Lightness (LIT) .... light (Lt)
Saturation (SAT) ..... strong-very strong (St-VSt)

"... a type of diamond... classified as Type Ib. These diamonds absorb strongly in the blue part of the visible spectrum, giving them an attractive yellow colour... such a diamond would be classified as a canary yellow by gemmologists... Natural Type Ib diamonds contain typically 100 parts per million (ppm) of isolated substitutional nitrogen [atoms]..."

A.T. Collins   1980

"... For a small proportion of natural diamonds most of the nitrogen is still present in this [single substitutional] form, and the crystals have a characteristic yellow colour. These are classified as type Ib diamonds and in some cases the colour may be described as canary yellow."

G.S. Woods   1986

Number 254
Weight .... 2.41 ct
Measurements .... 9.27 x 7.87 x 4.53 mm
Shape .... cushion
Cutting .... antique brilliant
Common Name .... grapefruit
Hue (HUE) .... greenish yellow (g-Y)
Lightness (LIT) .... very light (VLt)
Saturation (SAT) .... moderate-strong (Md-St)

"... of gemms and pretious stones... are materiall... inanimate bodies... being first qualities: such as are hardnesse, heavinesse, thicknesse, colour, and tast. These are the naturall faculties of gemms..."

T. Nicols   1659

Number 255
Weight .... 2.50 ct
Measurements .... 11.70 x 7.55 x 4.86 mm
Shape .... pear
Cutting .... modern brilliant
Common Name .... chameleon
Hue (HUE) .... greenish olive (g-OL)
Lightness (LIT) .... dark (Dk)
Saturation (SAT) .... weak-moderate (Wk-Md)

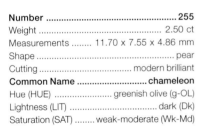

"... The crystals are nearly all green, varying from a suspicion of colour to dark olive..."

J.R. Sutton   1928

Number 256
Weight .... 2.53 ct
Measurements .... 9.05 - 9.27 x 4.66 mm
Shape .... round
Cutting .... antique brilliant
Common Name .... butterscotch
Hue (HUE) ....
.... yellowish orangish brown (y-o-BR)
Lightness (LIT) .... medium-dark (Md-Dk)
Saturation (SAT) .... moderate (Mod)

"... The test of the 'make' [cut] of a colored diamond is its appearance. If it lights up well over most of its surface and if the color is right [pleasing], one should not critcize the 'make' as one would be justified in doing in the case of a colorless diamond..."

F. Wade   1918

"... Diamonds... a variety presenting a cloudy or milky appearance resembling the opal, are sometimes met with."
S.M. Burnham   1886

"... milky diamond — a diamond that has a milky or hazy appearance. This condition usually is caused by clouds of exceedingly minute inclusions. Excessively fluorescent diamonds sometimes have a milky [hazy bluish] appearance in daylight..."
L.L. Copeland   1960

Number 257	
Weight .... 2.53 ct	
Measurements .... 11.38 x 8.17 x 3.51 mm	
Shape .... pear	
Cutting .... modern brilliant	
Common Name .... **opalescent**	
Hue (HUE) ...... bluish yellowish white (b-y-WH)	
Lightness (LIT) .... very very light (VVLt)	
Saturation (SAT) .... weak (Wk)	

"... A large diamond having a laminated texture... It possesess a very small degree of transparency, and is of a deep brown tint, which, owing to the density of the colour, gives the appearance of black."
J.L. Bournon   1815

"... the various shades of brown, first barely tinged, then gradually down through increasing coffee tints to mud..."
H. Bridgman   1916

Number 258	
Weight .... 2.77 ct	
Measurements .... 8.71 - 8.94 x 6.00 mm	
Shape .... round	
Cutting .... antique brilliant	
Common Name .... **coffee**	
Hue (HUE) .... brown (BR)	
Lightness (LIT) .... dark (Dk)	
Saturation (SAT) .... weak-moderate (Wk-Md)	

"... as a rule... the 'step-cut,' in one of its many forms, is most suitable for distributing color evenly..."
W.R. Cattelle   1903

Number 259	
Weight .... 2.83 ct	
Measurements .... 10.11 x 7.13 x 4.53 mm	
Shape .... elongated octagon	
Cutting .... modern step	
Common Name .... **topaz**	
Hue (HUE)	
.... pinkish orangish brown (pk-o-BR)	
Lightness (LIT) .... light (Lt)	
Saturation (SAT) ...... weak-moderate (Wk-Md)	

"... No fancy color diamond collection is complete without a green stone... most collections lack representation from the green portion of the diamond rainbow... green, while among the rarest of natural diamond colors, is the commonest of artificial ones — easily induced by irradiation. Yet connoisseurs spurn stones with lab-contrived color, instead dreaming of some day owning a green diamond with incontestably natural color..."
D. Federman   1990

Number 260	
Weight .... 2.88 ct	
Measurements .... 9.60 x 8.06 x 4.63 mm	
Shape .... cushion	
Cutting .... modified brilliant	
Common Name .... **celery**	
Hue (HUE) .... green (G)	
Lightness (LIT) .... light (Lt)	
Saturation (SAT) .... weak-moderate (Wk-Md)